A Man of Ideas

The Biography of Dr. Waldo Lonsbury Semon

Inventor of Plasticized Polyvinyl Chloride

Edited by Elizabeth M. Smith

A very special thanks to the following people for their dedication and help with this book:

Mrs. Mary Averill (nee Semon)
William F. Patient
Donald P. Knechtges
Dennison Advertising
Harris Rasic Design, Inc.
Olson and Gibbons, Inc.
Dr. Waldo Lonsbury Semon

The Geon Company
6100 Oak Tree Boulevard
Cleveland, Ohio 44131

Library of Congress Cataloging in Publication Data
Geon Company, The
Waldo Lonsbury Semon, A Man of Ideas
92-082985

FIRST PRINTING
Printed in the United States of America
10 9 8 7 6 5 4 3 2 1

Contents

*This book is the story of a man whose work has touched all our lives. Polyvinyl chloride has proven to be one of the most ubiquitous materials of the 20th Century. And, of course, it is the principal product of The Geon Company.**

Dr. Waldo Semon invented an industry. And in doing so he contributed mightily to the success of BFGoodrich for almost 40 years. But this book isn't about BFGoodrich or about its successor, The Geon Company. It's about a man who studied hard, fell in love, raised a family, traveled the world, laughed and lived throughout most of this century. There is a Chinese proverb, "May you live in interesting times." Dr. Semon not only lived in those times, his contributions played a significant role in making them interesting.

If you're a chemist, you'll find Dr. Semon's life fascinating. If you're not, you'll find it fascinating anyway, for Waldo Semon is truly a fascinating man. His genius and quick wit are an inspiration to us all.

William F. Patient
Chairman, CEO and President
The Geon Company

*On March 1, 1993, The BFGoodrich Company established its Geon Vinyl Division as a separate corporation called The Geon Company. On April 29, 1993, Geon became a public Company.

Introduction

Waldo Semon sits calmly on a couch in his small, one-bedroom apartment. Sunlight ricochets off the lenses of his glasses, glinting like the beginning of an idea.

It's entirely fitting; Dr. Waldo Semon is a man of ideas. In the world that surrounds him, thousands of products given life through his ideas are in everyday use. One wonders whether even his most immediate neighbors realize the role their bright, articulate friend has played in helping to wrap the world in vinyl.

Waldo Semon is the man whose ideas made vinyl possible.

Dr. Waldo Lonsbury Semon, retired director of corporate forward technology for The BFGoodrich Company, holds 116 U.S. patents (along with several in foreign countries) in the fields of rubber and plastic. He was the leader of the team that developed the first American synthetic rubber tire and is recognized as the pioneer of plasticized polyvinyl chloride and father of the $20 billion annual, worldwide vinyl industry.

These are times for reflection. Despite severe visual impairment, Dr. Semon jots down wide-ranging thoughts and memories from many years of an active, productive career. His involvement with the world of vinyl is now primarily that of a consumer; his contact with former colleagues, infrequent. But to anyone listening to his conversation, it's impossible to miss a lifelong curiosity in the world around him. A curiosity that ranges from plastics, rubber and chemistry to languages, quantum mechanics, history, philosophy and organoleptics.

Dr. Waldo Semon is still a man of ideas. A man apart from the norm.

This is his story.

"My forefathers were farmers, teachers,
writers, ministers, tinkers,
photographers and engineers.

My father was named Franklin
after Benjamin Franklin.

My first name and my father's middle name came
from family admiration of the writer
Ralph Waldo Emerson."

— Dr. Waldo Semon

1

Waldo Lonsbury Semon

"My father was an engineer with itchy feet.

A job came up just as he was completing college

and he left to go west even before being given

his diploma at commencement."

— Dr. Waldo Semon

Waldo Lonsbury Semon was born September 10, 1898, in Demopolis, Alabama, as the son of Franklin Emerson Semon and Flora Blanche Lonsbury Semon.

Frank Semon was an engineer, Michigan Agricultural College Class of 1890, and his work on various building projects kept the family on the move for much of Waldo's early years. In fact, the Semons departed from Demopolis as soon as Frank had finished building a power plant, cement factory and a house for his family.

The quest for engineering projects took the Semons from Demopolis to Hattiesburg, Mississippi; Philadelphia, Pennsylvania; Washington, D.C.; Augusta and Atlanta, Georgia; Birmingham, Alabama; Seattle, Washington; and Pomeroy, Ohio; with frequent side trips to Frank and Blanche's home town of Allegan, Michigan. Young Waldo was to live in a different place virtually every year until he entered college in 1916.

Waldo Semon is the product of two vastly different but equally fascinating families. Between them, they participated in practically every important movement in 19th century America.

His father's side of the family was explorers. Waldo's great-grandfather, David Semon, traveled across Central America during the time of the California gold rush, ending up as a cowboy on the West Coast. A tropical disease he encountered in Central America later caused him to return home to Michigan.

Waldo's paternal grandfather served in the Civil War and then soldiered under Custer against the Sioux. Two Semon uncles helped build the Great Northern Railroad.

Dr. Semon describes his mother's family, the Lonsburys, as "quite literary." His great-uncle, Henry Legett, an instructor at Vashon College in Washington state, had the most direct influence on young Waldo, endowing on him an

appreciation of literature and learning that has never abated.

Perhaps it was a combination of explorer's restlessness and a love of learning that spurred Dr. Semon to his eventual successes in discovering plasticized polyvinyl chloride, and 115 other patents while with BFGoodrich.

From an early age, Waldo was fascinated with books. His mother taught him to read, write and cipher before he was old enough to attend school. The family library included the usual Bible and almanacs, but what intrigued young Waldo most were his father's engineering text books from Michigan Agricultural College. They opened up the worlds of physics, mathematics, chemistry, surveying and mechanics – worlds he was never to stop exploring. Before reaching the fifth grade, he had committed huge passages of these books to memory.

Through his grandparents, Waldo was introduced to Shakespeare and to Sunday school readings at the local Baptist Church which he attended at the encouragement of his grandmother.

In these early years, Semon established what would become a lifelong habit of independent study and self-education. He describes hiding under the family chicken coop to read undisturbed.

His formal education actually began in 1904, at B.F. Day School in Fremont, Washington, a suburb of Seattle where Frank had found a job working for R.H. Thompson, Seattle's City Engineer.

Since he had already been reading and solving arithmetic problems for years, he was naturally ahead of his classmates and found himself bored much of the time. An understanding teacher allowed him to read and draw on his own. She introduced him to L. Frank Baum's magical land of Oz, an interesting contrast for a boy who was happiest drawing pictures of locomotives and other machines.

Not surprisingly, Waldo's curiosity ranged far beyond books. As an active boy growing up in the Pacific Northwest, he never tired of exploring the forests, rivers and mountains around him. He and his friends hiked and hunted the rugged wilderness outside Seattle, making occasional forays into the nearby Cascades. It was in Seattle that Waldo grew to appreciate a taste for salmon, which his father bought fresh and smoked from the neighboring Siwash Indians.

To help stretch his income and to keep the Semon family fed, Frank bought a milk cow, which grazed in the spacious backyard. Excess milk was sold, and it was Waldo's job to deliver it in a tin pail. The backyard was filled with gigantic Douglas Fir stumps, which created another way of stretching the budget. The boy stripped the bark and outer wood with an ax, and the family burned the wood in the kitchen stove.

"I changed my bedroom into an electrical laboratory.

I built a shocking coil and after I had tried it out on all the boys,

I connected it to the metal clothesline.

My grandmother was frightened to death when she touched the clothesline.

She thought she had had a heart attack!"

— Dr. Waldo Semon

By age nine, Waldo began performing his first experiments and engineering projects. The first were relatively safe. He fabricated a wet cell battery, using it to power a buzzer, which he also made.

Gradually, however, the projects became bolder and somewhat more hazardous. At one point Dr. Semon recalls trying to recharge dead telephone batteries by rubbing them on the electrified third rail of Seattle's commuter railway!

Waldo's cousin Russell was a frequent companion in those days, helping him build a roller coaster out of boards "appropriated" from fences near Russell's house on Latona Avenue. Semon remembers the roller coaster being tall and dangerous. But, like all things boys build themselves, the roller coaster seemed a lot larger than it really was.

The two boys teamed with a friend, Ofell Johnson, on another project guaranteed to send shivers up and down any mother's spine. Together, they cast several cannon barrels out of lead, and with black powder, fired wooden projectiles from the homemade artillery pieces. The powder was stored in a Mason jar, presumably under someone's bed. "Fortunately, we never hit anything. And more fortunately, come to think of it, we never got caught."

While not all of the young scientist's projects were so hair-raising, one did manage to alter the hair color of a certain Seattle feline. Waldo's Aunt Ellinger made the mistake of complaining that her white cat got dirty too easily. In fact, she said aloud, her cat would be better off black.

That was enough for Waldo. He dyed the cat, using a silver nitrate solution. The operation was a partial success, leaving the cat a mottled red, black and white. The real victim, though, was Aunt Ellinger's kitchen, the scene of the experiment. It seems the cat had objected to the dying process - rather strenuously, in fact - shaking off most of the dye, leaving the room's walls and ceiling covered with specks.

Such are the advantages - and drawbacks - of raising a young scientist.

"My father loved to sit on the front porch and play his violin.

He bought the cow because he thought that milking the cow would strengthen his hands for the violin.

It not only strengthened his hands, it also strengthened my back.

He made me carry the milk in pails to the people's houses."

– Dr. Waldo Semon

"He had a van Dyke beard, leather puttees
and pistols on each hip.

When he threw up cans,
he could hit them every time.

I already hunted rabbits with my Stevens single shot 22;
but after Colonel Cody showed us how to shoot,

it wasn't sporting to shoot a rabbit anymore

... unless he was on the run."

— Dr. Waldo Semon

2

An Inquisitive Lad

"I knew my numbers, could read and, after a fashion, write, by age six.

In school I was not interested in reading or arithmetic;

I already knew more than the rest of the class.

I liked to just sit and draw locomotives.

My teacher learned to keep me quiet by letting me draw and color geometric designs.

I also read fairy stories.

I read everything."

—Dr. Waldo Semon

The fledgling years of the 20th century were the perfect environment for an inquisitive lad who would one day forever alter the world around him.

The industrial revolution was entering its golden years. Henry Ford, who had begun Ford Motor Company in 1903, was looking over his shoulder just five years later at an upstart named General Motors. In 1909, a new material called Bakelite ushered in the plastics age.

These events would, in time, profoundly influence Dr. Semon's life and work. In 1909, however, they went unnoticed by an 11-year-old Waldo, who was preoccupied with his first job - not with plastics, but with pachyderms.

When Buffalo Bill Cody's Wild West Show hit Medford, Oregon, the Semon family's latest hometown, Waldo leaped at the opportunity to participate. He managed to land a job lugging buckets of water to thirsty elephants. His pay? Shooting lessons from Buffalo Bill himself!

The next summer, young Semon worked in Medford's electrical supply store. He would ride to and from work on a French-made, shaft-driven bicycle, a gift from his father.

Initially, his job was merely dyeing light bulbs red and green. Once the owner discovered the boy knew something about electrical work, however, Waldo was taken along whenever there was a new house to be wired. The electricians quickly learned that Waldo - who had been boring holes for the porcelain tubes in which the wiring was run - was adept at soldering and routing wires.

Waldo was in his element. He gladly did much of the work thereafter, while his older workmates were content to nap in the sun.

Brimming with energy, Waldo himself spent little time relaxing. Sometimes, though, late in the evening, he'd lie in the pasture near his home, gazing up at the stars speckling the Oregon sky. One object, appearing to be a bright star with a long tail, made its way across the heavens that summer. Waldo would later discover he had witnessed Halley's Comet. It was 1910.

That same year Waldo experienced his first ride in an automobile, a REO, owned by a Medford banker and father of one of his friends. Waldo walked away exhilarated, not suspecting the role he would someday play in the automotive industry.

Ashland, Oregon was the next stop for the restless Frank Semon. He began work planning and supervising the construction of a reservoir, a sewer system, and a sewage treatment plant in the city. Waldo had helped his parents and younger brother Darrell crate up the family belongings, but, since Ashland's first high school was still being built, he remained behind. He stayed with his Grandmother Lonsbury in Medford, attending high school there.

Waldo was becoming increasingly more inventive, turning his room at Grandma's into an electrical laboratory. He spent hour after hour tinkering with electrical experiments, some of which, to the chagrin of his friends, resulted in hair-raising pranks. Waldo was nonetheless managing to build a foundation of valuable scientific knowledge.

Grandma Lonsbury, the occasional object of her grandson's inventive horseplay, was somewhat grateful when young Semon left Medford for the newly completed high school in Ashland.

The latest Semon family abode in Ashland offered Waldo not only his own room, but laboratory space in a barn out back. He quickly set up the haphazard collection of lab supplies brought from Grandma Lonsbury's. Waldo tinkered in the solitude of his second floor laboratory — as the family horse frolicked below.

He continued to read all he could about electricity and wireless communication. Impressed by what he learned about scientist Nicola Tesla — who had pioneered alternating current less than two decades earlier — Waldo set his

"I used to walk up and down that platform with a magazine in hand,

and the others under my arm.

To sell them, I invented my own slogan:

'Only a nickel — half a dime — keeps you reading all the time!'

You'd be surprised how many magazines I sold with it."

— DR. WALDO SEMON

sights on building a radio transformer called a Tesla Coil.

His increasingly demanding experiments and inventions began to call for more and more money to support them. Waldo landed a job selling the *Saturday Evening Post* at Ashland's bustling train depot. The depot was the point on the Southern Pacific Railroad where crews were changed and engines added to take travelers up through Oregon's picturesque Siskiyou Mountains. Since all trains stopped for at least 10 or 15 minutes, Waldo never lacked for customers.

The Pacific Northwest continued to offer a perfect backdrop for Waldo's imagination and unquenchable thirst for knowledge.

From his desk at Ashland High School, he could gaze out over the picturesque Oregon mountainside. Bored by the school's elementary science program, he became more and more fascinated with studies of the world around him. Geography had become Waldo's favorite class. Much of the country surrounding Ashland was not yet populated, and he found the wilderness appealing.

On weekends he organized bicycle trips with friends. On occasion, the group would travel south toward the California border where they could see Mt. Shasta in the distance. There, Waldo found mineral and hot springs, and, to his delight, a cold spring bubbling with naturally carbonated water.

Friends in tow, Semon would bring his own lemon syrup, mix it with the spring's carbonated water, and make lemon soda. They would drink their fill, then head for the nearest warm spring for an afternoon swim. As he soaked, Waldo would speculate about the concentration of iron and sulfur in the water, and notice that both mineral content and water temperature affected the population of frogs, snakes and weeds in the springs.

Late that year, the budding scientist had to leave his barn laboratory and the hills of Ashland for Eugene, Oregon. His father had been offered the position of assistant city engineer.

The core of Waldo's high school learning was acquired over the next two years in Eugene. Courses in biology, German, mathematics and physics challenged his receptive mind. Interest-

"Some people move from one thing to another all their lives.

For me, once I knew it was chemistry, it was chemistry from then on.

Sometimes people ask me about my work. My work is chemistry.

Sometimes people ask me about my hobbies.

I tell them chemistry.

They ask me what I like to do in my spare time.

I tell them chemistry."

—DR. WALDO SEMON

ingly, the study of German would prove invaluable to his further education in chemistry, since the subject's many crucial texts were, at the time, available only in that language.

Waldo's knowledge continued to expand. Still, the trailblazer in him remained. He found expression for his adventurous nature at the local fairground, where he often raced the family horse against those of his friends. He could also be found running alongside his brother Darrell, who had become an accomplished long-distance runner. And he enjoyed bobbing along on the area's mill stream, paddling a canoe for hours on end.

Before Waldo finished high school, the Semon family moved twice, finally settling in Seattle. His nomadic life was over for the time being; he'd spend the next 10 years here.

The young scientist's imagination and ambition had remained far advanced for someone his age. In his senior physics class at the city's Lincoln High School, he presented a discussion on radioactivity, boldly predicting that one day the atom might provide power for the school. Semon was not only ahead of his class, he was ahead of his time.

After graduating from Lincoln High School, Waldo decided to work a year before considering further formal education. Seattle Harbor offered him his first full-time employment. Waldo helped place concrete piles, building a sea wall for the city's port. The job was temporary, however, and Waldo, using knowledge gained from his father, soon found work on a surveying crew.

As an assistant surveyor, Waldo learned to use a 500 foot survey chain with ease and draw blueprints with professional accuracy. His classroom? Miles of Washington's thickest brush.

Armed with these freshly-polished skills, Waldo landed a job in the summer of 1916 on a crew surveying land granted by the government to the Northern Pacific Railroad in the Cascade Mountains. The mission was to survey the land for accurate assessment of property taxes. The isolated, mountainous terrain had never been thoroughly charted.

It didn't take long for the head of the crew, an ex-army officer named Captain Long, to recognize Waldo's ability. At the conclusion of the interview, he offered the young surveyor a job as rear chainman — the second most important position in the party.

Spare hours were rare in the mountains, but Waldo made time to study. He had brought

a treatise on organic chemistry written in German and a British higher algebra textbook. To his surprise, he found his German thorough enough to make the chemistry text easier reading than the algebra book.

Surveying the Cascades was rugged and dangerous; at one point young Semon fell off a cliff and broke his shoulder. Still, he continued to work until early winter snows ended the survey team's work for the season.

Two events convinced Waldo to seek a college degree.

Applying for a coveted research position with the Bureau of Standards, he found himself spurned because he lacked a degree. He also interviewed with a Mr. Miller, one of the founders of Boeing Aviation. Miller offered him an immediate position with the firm, but strongly encouraged him to attend college.

Seeing the importance others placed on a college education, Semon enrolled at the University of Washington. His knowledge of engineering made it tempting to follow in his father's footsteps, but an aversion to the wandering lifestyle convinced him to pursue a different course. His love of chemistry led him to choose it as his college major.

"Some of the most remarkable things about the area were the valleys.

The snow got so deep during the winter that hunters would cut the limbs off the tops of trees as they passed on their snow shoes.

Come summer, it was strange to see trees with branches cut off 30 and 40 feet in the air.

It was like a giant had gone through the mountains."

—Dr. Waldo Semon

"When I graduated at 17, I think I was rather conceited ...
I had read most of the scientific books in
the University Carnegie Library
and the Seattle Public Library.

I could read a great deal of German.
I had been on the high school debating team, and had
read many of the decisions of the Supreme Court.

There was a great question in my mind
whether I should go to college at all

After all, college graduates were so stuffy."

— Dr. Waldo Semon

3

The University of Washington

When Waldo Semon entered the University of Washington in the fall of 1916, the First World War had been raging overseas for two years. Eventually, it would affect Waldo's life, as it would the lives of many young men.

But that autumn he was more concerned about being admitted to the University of Washington. Admission was complicated by the fact that Waldo's earlier indecision about college caused him to enroll after fall semester classes had already begun. He found himself petitioning one professor after another for permission to enter courses late.

The young man's intellect impressed the school's geometry and chemistry instructors, who felt that he could easily catch up to his classmates. The zoology and history professors were harder to convince. With reluctance, they finally gave in, allowing Waldo to enroll. Still, the history professor warned him not to be discouraged if he failed the course on the first try.

Semon's ability to accomplish many tasks in a short period of time now proved invaluable. He studied harder than ever, and passed all his courses that first semester, including — to the surprise of a skeptical professor — history.

Semon's family moved from Seattle before he started his freshman year at Washington. By necessity, he found a modest, second-story room at a local boarding house, owned by a Mr. Bidford, who was in charge of the university's sanitation department. To pay his rent, Semon persuaded Bidford to offer him a janitorial job in the three-story administration building.

At night and on Sundays, the young man swept floors, emptied trash cans and mopped floors. He dedicated the few remaining hours to his studies. But, because his roommate, a chemical engineering senior named Vic Larsen, would tease him about the amount of reading he

"In order to keep up, I had to study and do homework most efficiently

I had an 8 a.m. class every weekday, and also a lab on Saturdays, so time was of the essence.

I slept only four or six hours each night during the week, and tried to catch up on weekends."

— Dr. Waldo Semon

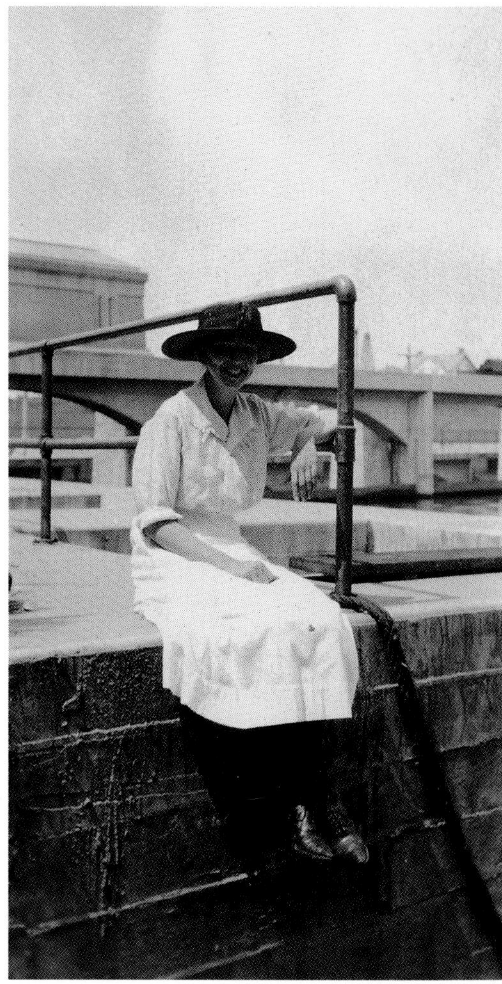

did, Waldo rarely studied in his room. To avoid Larsen's needling, he carried his books to the school's library. Larsen never suspected how fervently his freshman roommate studied that first year.

During his hectic schedule that first year, young Semon befriended two individuals who would have a profound affect on his life. One was an instructor; the other a classmate.

Chemistry lab professor Dr. Harlan Trumbull kindled the freshman's scientific imagination. Trumbull quickly became an inspirational role model. Struck by the teenager's intense dedication to science, Trumbull would remember Semon nine years later and recruit him for the significant role he was to play at BFGoodrich.

That first semester, Semon also met his future lifelong companion, Miss Marjorie Gunn. She sat several rows in front of him during chemistry class. After admiring her from afar for several weeks, Semon finally mustered the courage to ask her out. Gunn unceremoniously began the courtship by declining Waldo's invitation to the freshman mixer. Nevertheless, by the end of the year, a persistent Waldo had won her over. Although neither had much time for formal dating, they did manage to take in a new form of entertainment — the motion picture. Their first movie together: "The Birth of a Nation."

"She had long yellow hair that she braided and coiled about her head. I had a great deal of difficulty meeting her. She was so busy! But, by the time we saw the movie, she had grown somewhat used to me."

The next year, as a sophomore, Semon became increasingly more interested in mathematics. He was captivated by the childlike enthusiasm of math professor Dr. Eric Temple Bell. Bell was an Englishman who, when not lost in mathematical pursuits, dabbled in oriental philosophy and wrote novels.

Semon and Professor Bell became friends after the young man showed the mathematician a surveyor's trick for measuring the area under a curve with a two-bladed jackknife. They spent an entire class attempting to prove the mathematical accuracy of the method. Bell, who had little use for anyone not interested in mathematics, was awed by the young scientist's penchant for problem-solving. To Bell's delight, Semon's passion for chemistry had spilled over to mathematics.

By this time, the sophomore had moved from the second floor of the Bidford House to the basement. Vic Larsen had graduated in the spring and, because the upstairs room had more space, Semon agreed to let two other students room together there. He didn't mind; sleeping near the furnace had obvious advantages during chilly Washington state winters.

As usual, Semon ate breakfast and supper at the Bidford's. He ate lunch at the university. To save money that year, Semon chipped in with friends to cook lab-made creamed chicken, salmon and rabbit on biscuits.

In the summer of 1918, between his sophomore and junior years, the budding scientist had a change of heart concerning his major. Life as a research chemist would provide the stability he desired, but he wasn't excited about the prospect of pursuing knowledge for its own sake. He was much happier when he could see the practical results of his labor. He envisioned his discoveries being used in everyday life. After pondering for days in his basement abode, Semon decided to switch his major from chemistry to chemical engineering.

Young Semon was drafted into the Army in his junior year at Washington. The U.S. had declared war on Germany several months earlier. But because the conflict was introducing the world to modern technological warfare, the Army decided Semon's skills in chemistry and math would prove more useful in the labs of the University of Washington than in the trenches of Europe. He was assigned duty conducting research for Army Intelligence at the school.

Waldo's first assignment was in cryptography, and the Army's demands tested the young scientist's ability to solve problems quickly. The Army requested that he develop chemical agents

"At heart, I was really an engineer who was interested in science."

— Dr. Waldo Semon

for revealing invisible ink without destroying the paper. The assignment was critical, because enemy spies were successfully using invisible ink to convey crucial messages. Within three months, Semon had answered the Army's challenge by developing ink-revealing chemicals of varying degrees of strength. These chemicals — when applied to coded paper one degree at a time — would reveal the hidden message without disintegrating the paper. Semon's system was used by the military not only during the war, but for many years thereafter.

Semon's second assignment was considerably more hair-raising. Along with several of the school's professors, he was asked to develop an alternative method for producing TNT. Until then, the explosive's most important ingredient was being produced exclusively in the advanced laboratories of Germany. Although the fledgling scientist and his professors successfully produced an explosive which offered more yield, the young chemist considered the group's survival a greater accomplishment. He was relieved when the TNT experiments ended.

In the fall of 1918, the Army desperately needed trained surveyors and engineers overseas, so Semon was ordered to ship out to Europe. Fortunately, the war's end in November 1918 spared him the threat of combat.

With the war concluded, Semon would no longer receive the $21 a month he made while in the Army. His military earnings marked the first time he had ever been paid for his scientificwork.

His Army assignments also were over and Semon once again concentrated on his coursework, as well as his courtship with Marjorie Gunn. Both were now seniors, burdened with heavy course loads and looking forward to graduation. Free hours were rare. To compensate, Semon would sneak into one of Marjorie's labs, pretending to be enrolled in her class. Marjorie would brief him on what had been presented in the course's lectures, and he would perform the lab exercises with her. The instructor never suspected.

"The professor was an absent-minded German scientist. I'm sure he wondered why I came to lab but never attended his classes. At any rate, I got an excellent course in bacteriology."

By the time he graduated with a bachelor of science degree in chemical engineering, Semon had amazed the university's scientific community with his proficiency in the laboratory. He also had become an inspiration to his peers.

Semon was first in his major and ranked

"At one point, one of the professors was trying to vacuum-distill nitroglycerine right in the laboratory. It was pretty touchy, and he nearly scared the wits out of me."

— DR. WALDO SEMON

among the top 10 students in the University of Washington's graduating class of 1920. His desire to learn all he could about science caused him to seek further knowledge. He enrolled in Washington's graduate school, and set his sights on achieving a doctorate in chemistry with minors in physics and mathematics.

Science was not the only subject that interested young Semon that eventful year of 1920. He was now hopelessly in love with Marjorie Gunn.

"Marjorie commissioned her cousin, Arthur Gunn, who was also a chemical engineer, to investigate my background, character and overall suitability. I have no idea what he did, who he talked to or what he ever found out about me...but I must have passed."

In September of that year they married. Shortly afterward, Semon began his graduate courses. To support his education and new bride, he landed a job at Washington, teaching physical science. They lived in a home owned by a widow. In addition to the landlady, Marjorie's grandmother lived with them for two years. Not much privacy for the newlyweds, but an experience Semon remembers fondly.

"In those days, it was the way older people were taken care of. Plus, I always thought my grandmother-in-law had a lot to offer."

That spring, the new Mrs. Semon helped out by tutoring undergrads at the university.

Waldo is seated in the front row, third from the right.

"Most of the work that I've done has been based on mistakes.

You have to look at something many ways, and expect the unexpected."

— Dr. Waldo Semon

4

Graduate School

Unlike the rudimentary classes that bored Waldo Semon his first year at Washington, the university's graduate courses challenged his intellectual curiosity. He found himself exposed to new and exciting mathematic and scientific material, information that sparked hours of experimentation in the school's laboratories. Semon, whose intellect was impressing even the crustiest of the school's professors, embraced these new academic opportunities with wide-eyed enthusiasm.

The young man was surprised to discover that even a math professor, who had lulled him to sleep as a freshman, had come to life in graduate school classes. This unlikely mentor inspired Semon to appreciate mathematics more than ever, and led him to understand keenly the world of unseen particles, knowledge that would prove invaluable in the laboratory years later.

Despite intense academic demands, the budding scientist completed his first year of graduate school with relative ease. Unfortunately, his teaching assignments ended with the school year, and the 23-year-old Semon had to seek work.

The lingering post-war recession made jobs scarce in the summer of 1921. The construction industry, the field Semon had come to rely on for temporary employment, was hit particularly hard. Fortunately, a power company consultant named Whitwell, who was also a University of Washington professor, had been struck by young Semon's problem-solving abilities in the laboratory. Whitwell convinced his company that Semon would be an ideal candidate to perform experiments that could lead to the production of gas from local resources, such as coal, rather than from the imported coke and petroleum that was being used. Semon eagerly accepted the research position, even though it meant that the young couple would have to pack up and move to Everett, Washington, a small town to the north of Seattle, for the summer.

The job paid $50 a month. Semon worked evenings and early mornings, six days a week, conducting experiments when the power company was not operating.

The facility was perfect for producing gas in large quantities, the task for which it was designed, but was ill-designed for the experiments Semon would need to perform. To compensate, Semon brought in equipment and materials from outside, even installing meters and sampling lines himself. At one point during his experiments, a light oily residue suddenly developed in the gas lines. The fact that their friend Waldo Semon had gummed up the gas

mains of Everett, Washington, would have come as no surprise to his childhood buddies. But this scientific side-effect startled the power plant's managers. They breathed a sigh of relief when Semon finally remedied the situation.

After long, solitary nights of experimentation, Semon would come home exhausted to the tiny house the couple rented for $14 a month. There he would find Marjorie and her grandmother just waking to greet the new day.

The young couple was willing to sacrifice, knowing the experience Semon gained at the power plant was priceless. But his paycheck didn't go far. To make ends meet, Marjorie and her grandmother bought wheat from a neighbor and made cereal, muffins, bread — even coffee from the grain themselves. They bought milk and vegetables directly from local farmers and even sewed all their own clothes.

When they managed to eke out time for

recreation that summer, Waldo and Marjorie would pack a lunch and slip away into the scenic Snohomish County countryside for long hikes. Silent films were a favorite way to relax as well. Movie matinees in Everett were five cents in 1921.

Late that summer, young Semon's experiments at the power plant came to fruition; he was successful in developing a process for generating gas from local material. The procedure required the mixture of two types of readily available Washington coal. To make it work, however, the plant would have had to be significantly retooled. Plant managers were impressed, but agreed with Semon's recommendation that the idea be scuttled because it was not cost effective.

When he returned to the University of Washington that fall, Semon learned that his hard work had paid off in another way. The chemistry department staff, already convinced by Semon's accomplishments in the school's laboratories, had received word of his hard work, dedication, and resultant success at the Everett power plant. The staff — led by Professor Whitwell — wholeheartedly appointed him assistant chemistry instructor.

Semon had developed a reputation for discovering new and better ways of getting things done; ways that could save money, increase productivity and satisfy consumer needs. He loved scientific research, but his goal was to see its results used in everyday life. This results-oriented approach to problem-solving won him an increasing number of research jobs, as area industry, fueled by the industrial fervor of the day, sought to build better mousetraps.

This would all change in 1925 as the University of Washington was forced by state legislation to limit the use of its facilities for non-academic purposes. Money earned from research work in the school's labs was now to be handed over to the university and pooled into a general fund. The school's new, restrictive policies disillusioned the ambitious young scientist who was only making $1,800 per year. Not only would he lose a major source of income but, because the school also clamped down on pay raises and promotions, he was less likely to climb up the academic ladder quickly.

"Because the University allowed the chemistry faculty to utilize its laboratories for outside projects, I could do work-related research alongside the experiments I was performing for my dissertation.

Some of the chemistry department professors even called me to collaborate with them on their own special research projects."

— Dr. Waldo Semon

While slowly building a career, Semon and his wife purchased a small plot of land in Seattle that autumn of 1921, with money borrowed from Semon's Uncle Oscar. When he wasn't busily spending time with Marjorie, who was now expecting their first child, Semon drew plans for a modest house to be built on the property. In the summer of 1922, sandwiched between research jobs, he helped build their first house. The Semons became a family of three that summer. Their new daughter Mary monopolized the couple's affections until Marjorie Elizabeth came along in 1924.

The following year Semon was invited to speak at the American Chemical Society's summer conference in Los Angeles. On the voyage south, Semon weighed his career options. The journey gave him the opportunity to scout, first-hand, potential job opportunities. He visited the University of California at Berkeley, the Hawaiian Sugar Company, the Great Western Electrochemical Company and the California Institute of Technology.

"I was shown around Cal Tech by a fellow who was also a former student of Professor McMillan's at the University of Washington. The professor described him as 'a smart boy who was going somewhere.' My guide was Linus Pauling."

Struck by the cooperation between the chemistry and physics departments at Berkeley, Semon was even more impressed by the leading-edge research being performed at Cal Tech; especially the experiments employing X-rays to examine the structure of organic crystals.

"By the time I got to Los Angeles, I had decided when I got home, I'd mail a research proposal to the Cal Tech chemistry department. That proposal would call for investigation of the vapor pressure of organic compounds."

At the conference, the youthful scientist's prestigious counterparts listened earnestly to the talk he had prepared. Afterward, Semon mingled with many of the country's top scientific minds,

"Did I worry about the future?

Oh, I suppose I did. But, I was ambitious and not afraid to work.

I wanted twice as much as anyone else,

and I was willing to work twice as hard to get it."

— Dr. Waldo Semon

looking all the while for windows of opportunity. However, he found the possibilities for employment very limited. Returning home by train, he stopped to visit his father who was supervising the construction of a highway near Crater Lake, Oregon. Perhaps the engineer could offer some advice. While walking the long trail from Anna Springs to Crater Lake with his father, Semon pondered the future. He would return to the University of Washington for one more year of teaching, but was uncertain what would follow.

"Innovation is not just one thing from one person.

It's not just research. It's not just development.

It's not just marketability.

It's the combination of all these things,

and it's a dedicated group of people

all contributing to an idea."

— DR. WALDO SEMON

5

The BFGoodrich Company

Unknown to Semon, his future was actually taking shape two thousand miles east in Akron, Ohio at BFGoodrich. The company, recognized throughout the world for producing rubber products, had recently carved itself a niche in the competitive automotive supply industry by manufacturing quality tires.

Semon's former freshman chemistry professor, Dr. Harlan Trumbull, who was now managing chemical research at BFGoodrich, was exploring the possibility of creating low-cost, man-made materials that would mimic, and possibly someday replace, rubber.

Trumbull's hopes of developing these synthetic materials were not greeted with enthusiasm by the company's pragmatic president, who was fond of saying, "You can't compete with nature." Management grudgingly gave in to Trumbull's petitions after he made clear the possibility that competitors might develop commercially viable rubber substitutes first, thus threatening BFG's market share. This reasoning appealed to management's bottom-line thinking; they gave him permission to recruit a chemist to research the concept.

There were a number of bright minds at BFGoodrich to choose from, including one top-flight research veteran Trumbull felt certain was perfect for the assignment. The candidate, although willing, was overwhelmed by his own slate of pressing assignments. The company's other chemists were equally engrossed in their own research. He was forced to look elsewhere.

Trumbull remembered an ambitious student at the University of Washington, one who could grasp broad concepts and create workable solutions in a way few of his peers could. He recalled the demanding, even dangerous, military experiments the young scientist had performed and the student's ability to explore, develop and codify large bodies of chemical work. The student was, of course, Waldo Semon. Trumbull knew where he'd find the young man — tucked away in a laboratory somewhere at the University of Washington.

Trumbull's phone call in the spring of 1926 couldn't have come at a more opportune time. Semon, wrapping up his teaching and research work at the university, was still uncertain about his future. His proposal to the chemistry department at Cal Tech had fallen on deaf ears, and the alternatives were not encouraging. He accepted his former professor's offer with enthusiasm, immediately preparing for the journey east.

"To make ends meet, I was ready to establish a career in industrial research. I had high regard for Dr. Trumbull and trusted that he would not invite me if the opportunities were not good."

The logical means of travel would have been by rail, but the Semons recognized the possibilities for adventure. Here was an opportunity to experience first-hand the scenic wonders of an American west that not long before had been

"At the time there were only 500 miles of paved road between Washington and Ohio and they were mostly in the cities.

In Wyoming, there were three kinds of roads : dug roads, scraped roads and prairie trails.

We sure were glad to get into Hudson."

— DR. WALDO SEMON

peppered with forts and warring Indians. Semon bought a used, 1918 Ford touring car, rebuilt its engine and filled it snugly with Marjorie, his two daughters and six good spare tires. The trek, unfortunately, proved to be more arduous than enjoyable. The family drove along the lonely stretches of two-lane highway by day and slept in a small tent by night. Their old Ford complained loudly as they meandered through the Rocky Mountains.

Two weeks and 14 flat tires later, the family arrived in Hudson, Ohio. Years later, they would amusingly call their travel adventure: "The Odyssey."

Semon was greeted at BFGoodrich by Dr. Trumbull, who introduced his former student to the company's research and development staff, and proudly led him through bustling, well-equipped laboratories.

Semon found his initial challenge would be improving the materials currently being used by the company to bind rubber linings to metal tanks. He was to explore all possibilities, keying

in on developing the rubber-like materials Trumbull had envisioned. These synthetic compounds would have to be compatible with BFGoodrich's Vulcalock adhesive, a bonding substance that currently worked only in conjunction with natural rubber. The adhesive was formulated in 1918 by a clever BFGoodrich chemist. In seven short years, bonding rubber linings to industrial tanks and barrels had developed into a highly-profitable sideline for the tire-maker. Utilizing synthetic rubber, which would end dependence on outside rubber wholesalers and fickle market prices, would make it even more profitable.

To familiarize himself with the task at hand, Semon first worked with various forms of natural rubber, converting them into adhesives and then testing them on metal. He carefully noted how each product measured up to the current Vulcalock adhesive and kept Trumbull informed on the formulations that offered the most promise. After a number of successes with natural rubber, he turned his attention to developing the hoped-for synthetics that could replace it.

Because his curiosity drove him to peer into neighboring BFGoodrich laboratories, Semon soon became well-known to every scientist in the company. His appetite for knowledge also moved him to absorb every bit of information he could find on synthetics. He learned that a crude compound, known as "Oil of Dutch Chemists" had been discovered in 1795 in Holland. He also read that a chemist named Regnault — using his Dutch predecessor's discovery as a starting point

— formulated a sweet-smelling gas called vinyl chloride in 1834. This mixture was utilized by researchers in the late 1800s, who chanced upon what they considered a useless by-product: a durable solid that was unaffected by water or acids. A chemist named Ostromislensky would analyze the substance a decade later, recording its properties, but his research went no further. Lightly regarded at that time, this substance would soon change Semon's life forever.

To his delight, Semon discovered the BFGoodrich library to be rich in current information concerning synthetic rubber. Prompted by the invention of the automobile, the increasing demands of industry, and skyrocketing prices of natural rubber, chemists had been attempting to create usable rubber substitutes for more than 30 years. Poring over these findings, he was encouraged by the work of two Hood Rubber Company chemists named Earle and Kyriakides, who created synthetic rubber from organic compounds in 1908. Their discovery, hindered by an impractical process to eliminate impurities, was shelved because the end-product proved to be more costly than even the inflated natural rubber prices of the day.

During World War I, the German government, desperate because the country's supply of natural rubber was cut off, embarked on a crash program to develop synthetic alternatives. German scientists began where U.S. chemists had left off shortly before the war. They hoped to utilize organic materials to develop methyl rubber, the same synthetic material U.S. rubber companies had dismissed earlier because it was not cost-effective. Using coal and lime, the Germans achieved only minor success in attempts to make synthetic tires; a fact that even the Kaiser, whose limousine was raised by jacks to prevent flat spots from forming on the tires, was painfully forced to admit.

Motivated by what he read, Semon, wielding the same tireless tenacity that impressed his professors at Washington, dove head-long into the synthetics project. His objective: to work toward a synthetic rubber to replace the natural rubber currently being used to line industrial tanks. His energy would deliver him to the threshold of a discovery much more significant, a product that would help usher in a new industrial era —the age of plastics.

"Perhaps 99 percent of my experiments will be failures.

But, although they don't accomplish what I set out to do,

they still reach a truth...

something worthwhile."

— Dr. Waldo Semon

6

The Invention of Vinyl

Waldo Semon began his search for a cost-effective synthetic rubber adhesive by looking at vinyl materials formulated through polymerization, a procedure that creates, by condensing or adding molecules, a compound with a greater molecular weight. It was not a new idea; scientists had been studying vinyl polymers for more than 50 years. But no commercial use had ever been found for these compounds.

Semon hurried to the laboratory each day during that summer of 1926, hoping to find that he could turn these polymers into the desired synthetic rubber. However, intense experimentation caused his supply of a critical base substance to run out and he was forced to find a chemical to replace it. This setback would prove to be pivotal in his discovery of a dynamic new plastic material. He switched from bromide to a base of readily available chloride. The result, a far cry from the synthetic rubber he was groping for, turned out to be a wispy gas.

During his experiments to transform this gaseous product into a palpable substance, Semon's counterparts began to fear for their colleague's safety. Test tubes throughout the labs at BFGoodrich rattled, sometimes violently, as Semon's experiments resulted in explosions of varying degrees. Yet, Semon's dogged determination finally paid off. He produced a tangible powder that, when introduced to hot solvents and then allowed to cool, turned into a flexible gel with a rubbery quality. He marveled at his creation, polyvinyl chloride, a substance that would soon be known around the world as PVC or vinyl.

Semon found the material could be reheated into a pliable solvent and cast to make any shape. Intrigued with its practical potential, he molded it into a shoe heel to test its durability. He discovered that the compound would not conduct electricity, and that it was also waterproof. These findings moved him to coat a screwdriver, a pair of pliers and electrical wire with the vinyl plastic. He was elated with the results.

"As I worked with these gels, their properties intrigued me more and more. The possibilities were so fascinating that, for a time, the original problem of finding a synthetic rubber adhesive for Vulcalock, was forgotten. I even molded a golf ball from an exceptionally rubbery composition and bounced it down the halls of BFGoodrich, showing it to the other scientists. Everyone thought it was interesting, but it wasn't what I was supposed to be working on."

Hoping that this innovative material might offer alternatives to Vulcalock, Semon tested it on drums and barrels. Despite various attempts, he could not formulate a batch of PVC that would bond well to the metal from which these chemical containers were made. He finally spot-welded a screen to the inner surface of a small drum, coated the screen with a paste of powdered PVC and plasticizer, and heated it to line the tank. The lining was resistant to acids, but

"To test the strength and purity of Carbide & Carbon's PVC,

I threw a tumbler against the floor with all my strength.

It bounced to the ceiling and came down

directly on the bald head of one of my colleagues

Neither head nor tumbler broke."

—DR. WALDO SEMON

the bond was impractical. Frustrated in his attempts, Semon eventually returned to the task of developing adhesive linings made of natural and synthetic rubber — a project that would end eight years and 100 successes later. But his interest in polyvinyl chloride plastic refused to wane. He continued his research on the new compound, dividing his time between it and the Vulcalock experiments.

By the late 1920s, Semon had become well-acquainted with the varying aspects of his creation and its chemical properties, as well as the varying processes that could produce it. Although BFGoodrich had achieved some success finding commercial uses for polyvinyl chloride, including PVC shoe heels and PVC-coated chemical racks, the curious material was still a misfit in an American marketplace accustomed to products made of natural rubber. More marketable uses would have to be developed, and the possibility of inventing an altogether new, PVC-based product that could introduce the innovation to a broader public would need to be explored.

In the frightening atmosphere of the stock market crash of 1929, though, the idea of sinking money into an odd substance with no proven track record seemed foolhardy to some decision-makers at BFGoodrich. Edgy and impatient, they expressed concern about the mounting costs of developing PVC and began to question its ability to earn a profit. What business, they asked, did a rubber company have developing an entirely new market, especially for a non-rubber product?

To prevent the company from abandoning the project, Semon was forced to devise a workable solution. One weekend at home, observing Marjorie dividing her time between sewing and looking after their newborn child, Constance Anne, the scientist was struck by a revelation. Watching Marjorie sew new curtains reminded him that polyvinyl chloride could easily coat anything — even fabric. It could even be used alone, without fabric, to make shower curtains. Here was the new, potentially lucrative product that company management had been clamoring to see!

Several days later, Semon, now director of research and development for PVC, was ordered to update one of the company's vice presidents on the progress of the project. In a meeting that just a week earlier could have ended his work with polyvinyl chloride forever, Semon greatly impressed his skeptical superior. He displayed PVC-coated swatches of the fabric Marjorie had used in her household curtains. He pointed out that the transparent vinyl covering did not detract from the cloth's brilliant colors, and emphasized that the material was completely waterproof.

"I took the fabric and placed it over the mail in his mail basket, and poured water in the depression ... it did not leak. The vice president, a camper, who was used to being dripped on by so-called waterproof tents, was duly impressed. I have often wondered what would have happened to the PVC program if the mail had gotten wet."

Semon's discovery found a receptive market as vinyl-coated umbrellas, raincoats, and shower curtains hit the store shelves in 1931. Spurred by the sudden dramatic success of its PVC-based products, the company built a coating plant to handle increasing consumer demand. Sales were so brisk that BFGoodrich, unable to produce the quantities of basic PVC material required, asked a chemical supplier named Carbide & Carbon to develop a large-scale manufacturing process for the compound. The chemical company had been waiting several years for BFGoodrich to create a marketable product, one that would justify producing large quantities of polyvinyl chloride. The breakthrough plastic was now in mass production.

Company researchers found another use for polyvinyl chloride, this time in the lucrative automotive supply industry. PVC, it was

discovered, offered a much-improved seal for lubricant-filled shock absorbers. Soon after, BFGoodrich's director of research, J. W. Schade, tagged all PVC products with the trade name,

"Koroseal®," a term which became a registered company trademark. Hidden away in the laboratory, Semon's monumental experiments in polyvinyl chloride plastics had gone unnoticed by the world around him. But, soon after the Koroseal name was established, his efforts gained notoriety. He was celebrated in trade publications, including *Industrial & Engineering Chemistry* and *Business Week* magazines. One article, co-written by Semon himself, was titled "Koroseal®, A New Plastic." On October 10th, 1933, Semon's commitment and perseverance were rewarded. He was granted the original patent for PVC by the U.S. Patent and Trademark Office — U.S. patent 1,929,453.

"Most of the work that I've done

has been based on mistakes.

You have to look at something many ways,

and expect the unexpected."

— Dr. Waldo Semon

Synthetic Rubber

Although natural rubber, isomer, "synthetic rubber" and PVC are all plastics, they should not be confused. Each is most suitable for a specific purpose. The invention of PVC did not hinder the search for a synthetic rubber compound. Producing tires from synthetic materials had been a dream of tire manufacturers since the first days of the automobile. By the mid-1930s, a commercially viable tire formed of man-made compounds was still a fantasy. BFGoodrich management was determined to convert this dream into reality.

They realized that the future of the American tire industry was in synthetics. More importantly, the turmoil in European politics raised the possibility of another world war, where synthetic materials might play a key role. The Nazis were engaged in a thinly disguised campaign of military building, and Hitler's scientists were attempting to manufacture synthetic rubber. Should conflict break out, the demand for natural rubber would exceed supply, and readily available sources would be cut off. Fearing that, BFGoodrich executives summoned the man who had established a proven track record for solutions — Dr. Waldo Semon.

After years of investigating rubber substitutes for the Vulcalock project, Dr. Semon was well-versed in the basic aspects of synthetics research. He was knowledgeable not only of its history but also its innumerable possibilities. A laboratory veteran, he was equally well-schooled in the frustrations synthetics could provide, as many of his earlier experiments had failed to achieve usable results.

Dr. Semon knew the basic challenge in developing a synthetic-rubber tire would be overcoming the obstacle of impurities. With the same determination that had converted his research of PVC plastic into a commercial success, Dr. Semon attacked the problem of creating a synthetic tire.

"The problem could not be solved quickly. I spent the first six months reading, visiting other companies and evaluating the field. My endeavor could not be made public because that would have made it more difficult for me to secure information from outside sources, compelling other companies to engage in similar projects." His ability to read French and German allowed him to gain insight into research being done in the European laboratories. After six months of study, Dr. Semon had gleaned the crucial details of five of the most promising experiments. From these, he chose a formulation that could be produced most cost-effectively with an easy-to-manufacture petroleum base.

The scientists developing this synthetic material were keeping their project shrouded in secrecy, so Semon was unable to learn exact details about basic procedures. As a result, he would need to create his own process. Turning vague notions into synthetic rubber was only half the challenge. From there, the material would

have to be transformed into a durable tire that could easily be mass produced. Then, of course, there was also the question of whether a demanding public would accept it. His work had just begun.

First, he needed raw materials, the basic building blocks to perform his research. BFGoodrich laboratories were not capable of producing these substances,including the petroleum version of a critical material called butadiene, on a large scale. Despite the need to keep the project a secret, Semon was forced to enlist the support of outside industrial scientists. He was gratified to discover that even competing companies, amidst an atmosphere of impending national crisis, were willing to give up short-term goals and cooperate.

His own BFGoodrich colleagues were also eager to participate. Semon assembled some of the company's brightest minds, scientists who also could be trusted to keep the project a secret. In 1936, work began in earnest.

Far from exhilarating, the early stages of experimentation were monotonous, tiresome exercises. Possible synthetics were prepared, purified, evaluated and then summarily dismissed, one after another. The task was immense. It soon became apparent that instant results, even within the intense research environment that Semon had initiated, were impossible. By 1937, Semon's staff had discovered only a

"The people had to be convinced that synthetic tires would hold up.

So we only provided synthetic rubber tires to company presidents and board members.

And that convinced them."

— Dr Waldo Semon

handful of possibilities. Enthusiasm waned as the undertaking began to lag behind its hopeful schedule.

In a daring attempt to speed up the project, BFGoodrich convinced the German government to welcome Dr. Semon that year as an ambassador of science. Operating within this guise, Semon scoured every scrap of information he could about Germany's synthetic rubber program, hoping to find data that would accelerate his own research.

Hailed as the father of polyvinyl chloride, he was introduced to leading German chemists and physicists who, not surprisingly, were just as eager to learn from him all they could about PVC. Semon was permitted to examine finished products of PVC and the German's latest attempts at developing synthetic rubber. Wary of his motives, however, the Germans refused to allow a visit to any manufacturing or research facilities, claiming such visits would be inconvenient. They also had him followed throughout the whole journey. At one point, he recalls accidentally leaving a package in a taxi. The package subsequently showed up at his hotel.

"My Nazi hosts didn't know I could understand their language. So, when they spoke to one another in German — unwittingly thinking that I could not understand a word — they gave away information that they didn't want me to have."

Returning to the U.S., however, Semon was forced to admit to his colleagues that he was unable to uncover critical information about the German synthetic rubber program, save that the Nazis were frightfully ahead of their own efforts. Yet, he remained optimistic, hoping the U.S. synthetic would not only soon become a reality, but would exceed its German counterpart in quality. Semon had also come to the conclusion that Germany's escalating militarization would eventually lead to war. Management quickly agreed with his recommendation that the project be greatly accelerated.

Dr. Semon's courageous foray into Germany, although not providing a specific solution to creating man-made rubber, breathed new life into a project desperately in need of vigor. More scientists were brought in, and special mixing machines, which shook up to 100 test tubes in unison, were created. Amidst a blur of determination and the whir of mixers, Semon's staff formulated more than 14,000 petroleum-based, synthetic rubbers. Still, after nearly a quarter million tests, the end results were always the same — impurities sabotaged the materials.

At home during this period, it was not unusual for Marjorie to find her husband lost in thought, attempting to dream up a radical new approach. While listening to a phonograph he had pieced together himself and installed in the living room, Dr. Semon would weigh the most minute details of an experiment, hoping to unlock the secret to a practical synthetic rubber.

Finally, the long-sought solution appeared. Noting that impurities were sometimes present in his materials for polymerization, he decided to regulate the phenomenon, adding controlled amounts of foreign substances during this critical point in the experiment. One, a sulfur compound, provided a controlled polymerization that led to superior workability in the finished product.

Here was Semon's breakthrough! The new synthetic compound was far superior to any that Semon and his colleagues had seen. Thrilled, Semon reported his discovery to John Collyer, who had become the company president in 1939. Collyer gave the go-ahead to mold the compound into tires. Testing of production methods soon began in one of BFGoodrich's smaller plants.

One by one, the obstacles to large-scale production were attacked and eliminated. Not only would the tire, which was made from a combination of Semon's new synthetic material and natural rubber, hold up to road conditions, it would last for an unheard of 50,000 miles. Semon and his dedicated group had successfully created America's first mass production, synthetic rubber tire. BFGoodrich gave Dr. Semon's new synthetic rubber the trade name, "Ameripol®," and called the tires made from it "Liberty Tires."

On June 5th, 1940, at an introductory celebration in New York city's Waldorf-Astoria Hotel, BFGoodrich proudly unveiled Dr. Semon's discovery to a group of leading industrialists. Fascinated, many wondered aloud about the role the tire might soon play overseas, where Germany, just nine months earlier, had invaded Poland.

"I've always tried to find the truth.

It's almost like an accident

suddenly it's right there,

and we can all agree on it."

— DR. WALDO SEMON

8

Life During Wartime

By the spring of 1941, the conflict in Europe had spread. Great Britain and Canada had been fighting the Nazis for more than a year, and Japanese aggression in the Pacific was now cutting off sorely needed supplies of natural rubber. World War II was underway.

To meet increasing demands for synthetic rubber products and to prepare for its possible entrance into the war, the U.S. government called on the nation's leading rubber companies. The plan was to sidestep dependence on foreign supplies of natural rubber by mass producing a synthetic substitute. Representing a monumental breakthrough in synthetic rubber, Semon's Ameripol® was crucial to the plan. After several meetings with U.S. government officials, BFGoodrich agreed to share the formula with competing businesses, many of whom had no background whatsoever in synthetics. Inspired by Semon's accomplishments, researchers from these companies displayed a high degree of respect for the scientist. Many had even used some of his earlier procedures in their own laboratory experiments. By electing him First Technical Committee Chairman, they authorized him to orchestrate the demanding scientific duties of this multi-company government program into synthetics research.

The formerly confidential manufacturing procedures used at BFGoodrich to make synthetic tires, including the Ameripol patents, were now poured into a pool. Fearing espionage, the government granted access to the formulas only to those directly involved with the project. As technical chairman and the only BFGoodrich representative with a top-secret clearance, Semon was the sole researcher entrusted with classified information. He was frequently called to Washington, D.C. to provide updates.

Ameripol — and the manufacturing processes Dr. Semon and his BFGoodrich team had created to produce it — would prove critical in the development of "GR-S," an improved, highly durable synthetic rubber that would soon compose the tires of all U.S. military vehicles.

"I had to testify before the Truman Committee, a committee that I think investigated everything. I'm a compulsive note-taker so I was writing everything down when Senator Truman made me stand up and bawled me out, saying, 'There'll be only one record of this hearing.'"

As 1941 drew to a close, many Americans remained hopeful that the United States would avoid being drawn into the war. But the Japanese attack on Pearl Harbor on December 7 quickly ended this optimism. Military demands for products made from Dr. Semon's innovations suddenly escalated. But BFGoodrich had, in less than a year, increased by tenfold its capacity to manufacture synthetic rubber.

Prior to the war, Semon's discoveries had been turning up steadily in products across America. Now, they would play a critical role in military equipment used around the world.

The U.S. military swiftly embraced Semon's innovations. Vinyl plastic, synthetic rubber, and even the bonding processes developed as part of the Vulcalock project all found uses during World War II. GIs could find vinyl in ponchos, tents, tarpaulins, rafts, gun covers, hospital sheeting, raincoats and other gear. It proved useful in making leak-proof fuel tanks as well. PVC, because of its flame retardance and good weatherability, was also used to insulate wiring strung throughout Navy ships and U.S. warplanes. As the Pacific conflict intensified, taking its toll on an alarming number of Navy vessels, demand for the compound increased. Pressured by the Navy's seemingly endless need, BFGoodrich's Louisville, Kentucky, plant would soon be producing more than 1,500 tons of PVC per month.

Braced by the synthetic tire project it began before entering the war, the United States found itself well-prepared to utilize Semon's compounds. With a number of tire makers capable of

"During the war, every pound of PVC resin we could produce,
was allocated for essential military use.

And by 1945, U.S. production of synthetic rubber was greater than the highest
pre-war yield of natural rubber.

Extended into a solid band two inches in diameter,
this synthetic material would be long enough to reach from the moon
to the earth, with enough left over to encircle the earth at the equator."

— DR. WALDO SEMON

manufacturing the material, mass production of synthetic rubber was well under way. Manmade, synthetic tires could be found on Jeeps and trucks in every theater of the war.

The frustrating years Semon spent adhering linings to industrial tanks also paid off during the war. One of his discoveries, a process for bonding brass to rubber, proved vital in the manufacturing of tank treads. The innovation, which he had patented in the early '30s, permitted allied tanks to get far greater mileage from a set of treads than the dreaded German Panzers. It was an advantage that infuriated Nazis in the heat and sand of northern Africa.

In 1943, BFGoodrich, impressed with Dr. Semon's capacity to coordinate the scattershot group of companies that made up the government synthetics project, awarded their top scientist the post of Director of Pioneering Research. In this capacity, Semon was given free rein to investigate any area of research that interested him. Despite administrative responsibilities, which included numerous speaking engagements, Semon earned 30 patents during the war. He would later admit, half-jokingly, that he never worked for more than 20 hours a day. In 1945, *Future* magazine hailed Dr. Semon as one of the greatest scientists in the world.

"I never worked for more than 20 hours a day."

— Dr. Waldo Semon

9

Post-War Synthetics Demand

Soon after the Japanese surrendered in August of 1945, ending World War II, Semon was asked by BFGoodrich management to tackle yet another task. Noting the number of products spawned by the necessities of war, management was certain that successful commercial applications could be found for them. Semon, who had become legendary for an ability to spot potential in the most humdrum of compounds, assembled a staff and began sifting through thousands of records.

There were more than 14,000 formulations of synthetic rubber alone. The search, arduous and time-consuming, produced what some might consider modest results. But Semon, having found five new commercial possibilities from the stack of synthetics research, deemed the project a complete success.

BFGoodrich, unable to convince the U.S. Patent Office to allow it to maintain sole ownership of PVC resins and product development during wartime, found itself competing with other PVC manufacturers after the war. But the company, owing partly to Dr. Semon's stature as the product's inventor, remained the nation's leading PVC resin manufacturer.

During the late 1940s, the demand for PVC resins suddenly exceeded supply as a host of new applications reached the consumer market. The vinyl plastic was now being used to make shower curtains, upholstery, pocketbooks, and "patent leather" shoes. BFGoodrich, which now sold PVC resins under the trade name the company still uses today, "Geon®," was successful during this period marketing rug backings and shelf-paper made from the plastic. By 1947, polyvinyl chloride was molded into garden hoses, a product not expected to win much more than a modest profit. Produced from pure PVC rubber-like plastic, this unlikely candidate for success sent sales of PVC resins skyrocketing and cleared the way for numerous other products, including vacuum cleaner bumpers, appliance gaskets, fender guards and electrical plugs. With new uses for his invention developing daily, Semon was now referred to affectionately by his peers as the man who had wrapped the world in vinyl.

His wartime obligations behind him, Dr. Semon found more time to spend with Marjorie and their three daughters, who had grown up while he was buried in his experiments. Mary had graduated from college with a degree in chemistry, and her sisters were displaying a keen interest in science as well. Like the trial and error method he employed in the laboratory, Semon followed a similar process at home trying to arrange convenient moments to spend with his busy family. When they did manage time together, the Semons would spend leisurely hours picnicking in the woods near their home, or boating on Silver Lake. When his wife and children were away, Semon would relax in his favorite chair, dreaming of new ideas while listening to his hand-built phonograph.

But BFGoodrich had other plans for Dr. Semon. With the potential of overseas markets growing dramatically, the company implemented a strategy for worldwide expansion in the late '40s. The company had achieved success at home by opening sales offices shortly after the war in New York, Boston, Chicago, and Los Angeles. Markets for PVC and synthetic-rubber tires had yet to be fully developed in Europe, however, and BFGoodrich was eager to capture its share. Known throughout the world for his discoveries, Semon was selected by the company to represent it overseas in a dual role of spokesman and technical advisor.

Ten years after his journey through the laboratories of Nazi Germany, Waldo Semon returned to Europe in 1947. This time, because the trip was part business, part vacation, Marjorie traveled with him. The Semons toured England first, then flew to Holland, where BFGoodrich was building a new manufacturing plant. His scientific counterparts in Holland were overjoyed with his visit, eager to learn all they could from the man who invented PVC plastic.

Four years later, in 1951, Dr. Semon again returned to Europe. This time the trip was strictly business. With the U.S. now at war with North Korea, military demands for PVC plastic were again increasing, and developments in plastics overseas might prove useful. Semon's mission was to evaluate them and bring back any with military or consumer potential.

The visit, which entailed not only information gathering but negotiating licensing for the most promising of the processes, proved demanding, both physically and intellectually. But Semon enjoyed challenges. He stopped at research facilities in six European countries.

Cold War distrust between the U.S. and the Soviet Union caused Dr. Semon to avoid Soviet satellite countries, fearing that critical information might somehow be leaked.

Encouraged by the success of his 1951 visit, BFGoodrich sent Semon to Europe once again shortly after the Korean War ended in 1953. This time, he hoped to find notable developments in plastics in the scientific programs of West Germany. By focusing his efforts within one country, Semon felt he could spend more time scrutinizing promising procedures. To his surprise, the Germans now lagged behind the U.S. in plastics and synthetics technology. Semon, who was directed by BFGoodrich to scout for promising young scientists while on these trips as well, would make several more journeys to Europe throughout the '50s.

"I remember one particularly bright young scientist from Purdue named Haas who was

"The Russians had a reputation for being able to make people talk.

Because of my top-secret clearance during the second world war,

I possessed some pretty interesting information ...

facts the Russians would have found very interesting, too.

We were afraid that this vital information would fall into the wrong hands."

—DR. WALDO SEMON

working on a chlorine manufacturing process. Since PVC is more than 50% chlorine, you can see how important that would be. BFG supported his research while he was a student. Then when he graduated, he went to Dupont for a salary larger than that of his Purdue instructors."

With a fresh generation of bright young scientists seeking uses for PVC plastic, new technologies and products were rapidly emerging. To the delight of consumers, the compound continued to show up in a variety of surprising ways. Plastic toy soldiers, radio cases, princess phones — and parts for another new invention, the television — were just a few of the items in which PVC could be found.

Although he continued research into synthetic materials, Semon's experiments centered primarily on developing more efficient chemical fertilizers as the 1950s drew to a close. An ambitious attempt to slow the ripening process of bananas during shipment was abandoned because the latex coating emitted a foul odor. He persevered with other biochemical experiments in the early 1960s, achieving minor victories with formulations that successfully controlled apple scale and prevented disastrous winter kill in pine trees.

"I decided that I would get what I wanted from life

not by taking it from society,

but by adding to the standard of living.

I was willing to work to do that."

— Dr. Waldo Semon

10

Life After BFGoodrich

After nearly 40 years with the company, Dr. Waldo Semon retired from BFGoodrich in 1963. To him, retirement was merely a technicality brought on by his 65th birthday; he remained as active as ever. Not only did he continue to work for BFGoodrich in a consulting capacity, but he also fulfilled speaking engagements, wrote articles on the history of polyvinyl chloride and prepared reports on the future of plastics for various professional societies.

BFGoodrich was hard-pressed to keep up with the increased demand for PVC resins, which were now available in a variety of vivid colors. Flashlights, dashboards, portable record players and instant cameras were just some of the products made from the brightly shaded plastic. Toys made from plastic compounds were now being produced at home by youngsters, as plastic molding kits hit store shelves.

Fashion designers took note of plastic as well, designing go-go boots and vinyl dresses from the material Semon had invented 40 years earlier.

Not long after retiring from BFGoodrich, Semon was offered a teaching post at Kent State University. He welcomed the chance to be with young people again. He wondered about how the technological advances over the last few decades had impressed young people, some of whom would now be his pupils. He was still eager to learn himself and enjoyed the fact that the post would also allow him to keep up-to-date on scientific research and discoveries.

While guiding his young students through various research assignments, Dr. Semon was amused to discover them using the word "plastic" as a slang term for anything that wasn't the genuine article. He realized that his innovations, with their ability to cost-effectively replace virtually any item, had changed forever the way people live.

By 1971, Dr. Semon's eyesight had deteriorated. In an environment filled with volatile chemicals, vision was crucial. He suddenly found that he had no other choice but to leave his teaching position at Kent State. Nearly blind,

Semon fought to maintain what vision he had remaining. Soon after leaving the university, the 73-year-old braved surgery. The operation, performed by specialists in Cleveland, was a modest success. But it only partially restored the sight of a man who once impressed Buffalo Bill with his deadeye shooting.

Dr. Semon would not be deterred; he continued his brisk agenda, swapping teaching duties for community activities. He served as a board member for Akron's Park System. Not long after his operation, Dr. Semon, who was still respected throughout the tire industry for his keen knowledge of manufacturing processes and patents, was approached by the Firestone Rubber Company. Firestone needed an outsider's opinion on key projects, as well as someone with knowledge of patent laws. Semon was well-known to the company for his research at BFGoodrich and was a welcome addition in the role of consultant.

One year later, while between assignments for Firestone, Semon again found it necessary to travel to Europe. This time, he was called to Sweden to help mend an awkward system of conflicting patent laws. As a consultant, Dr. Semon offered various options to Swedish industrial law makers, who were impressed with his suggestions. Some of those ideas were implemented as the country unified its patent laws. Nearly 10 years after formally retiringfrom BFGoodrich, Waldo Semon was still hard at work.

As tire manufacturers struggled for slivers

of market share in an industry deluged with competition, Semon's expertise was called upon during the 1970s to protect various patent positions. He gave testimony on patents before federal judges in Cleveland, Baltimore and other cities. In one memorable patent infringement case, Semon was asked to defend Firestone's formulations for a key compound. Another tire maker had claimed the formulations were similar to its own. Dr. Semon testified that the formulations, while similar, behaved differently, and thus could not be the same. A federal judge ruled in favor of Firestone's competitor, but, after subsequent expert testimony from Dr. Semon, an appeals court reversed the decision.

"When it came time for me to testify, the federal judge called me before him, and softly said he had already made up his mind to rule in favor of the other tire maker, but he could not prevent me from testifying. Later, I was shown the car the judge drove ... it had the competitor's brand of tires."

Firestone lost the case, but then won on appeal. "I don't think anybody got any money out of it...except the lawyers."

Inspired by the biochemical experiments he performed at BFGoodrich shortly before retiring, Semon eventually bought a plot of land near Hudson, Ohio and grew soybeans, corn and tomatoes from its fertile soil. He also raised chickens on the modest farm, only a short drive from the Semon's Tudor-style house — which they referred to fondly as Brandywine Cottage.

As the '70s drew to a close, Dr. Semon divided his free hours between working his land and writing his memoirs. In 1979, Marjorie — who had remained by his side during the lean days in Washington, encouraged him through the years of frustrating experiments and wartime demands at BFGoodrich, and supported him while he wrestled with his fading eyesight — passed away.

She understood and tolerated me as no other woman would. And that was a great thing.

She was a part of me and when she died, I was only part of a person."

The man with the insatiable thirst for knowledge, who frazzled numerous teachers with endless questions as a student, received a bit of his own tonic while informally teaching youngsters from a nearby high school in the early 1980s. Covering a variety of topics with small groups of students, youngsters awed by his

accomplishments, Dr. Semon was bombarded with questions. Overjoyed with the opportunity to share his knowledge, he responded with childlike zeal, always encouraging his audience to seek further schooling. The experience reminded him of the role education had played in his own life, and the decision he nearly made 60 years earlier to survey the Washington mountainside, rather than suffer the indignity of becoming one of those stuffy college graduates.

"I suppose I've given hundreds of talks and she not only edited them all, she had to sit through practice runs on all of them.

She kept journals of our trips; I found them after she died.

I had someone read them to me and I felt like I was taking the trip all over again."

— Dr. Waldo Semon

"I've always tried to find the truth.

It's almost like an accident

suddenly it's right there,

and we can all agree on it."

— Dr. Waldo Semon

Creative Genius

"I was proud to be a part of the beginning of an industry.
Now I'm proud that the company I worked for has changed its name
to reflect my invention.
The Geon Company is a darn good name."

— Dr. Waldo Semon

The results of Dr. Semon's determination, creative genius and endless hours of hard work can be seen everywhere today. From bottles to volleyballs to vinyl siding, computer keyboards, appliance parts, piping and automotive components, the products generated from PVC are countless. And, to make things complete, in 1993 BFGoodrich spun off its Geon Vinyl Division into a publicly held corporation called The Geon Company.

Synthetic rubber tires are in every driveway and have helped set records at Indianapolis Motor Speedway. Dr. Semon's innovations will enable The Geon Company to continue as an industry leader in polyvinyl chloride technologies. A $20 billion industry, PVC is now the second most widely used plastic in the world, with global production of its resins exceeding 40 billion pounds.

The man who, as a child, shocked his grandmother with an electrified clothes line and gummed up the gas lines of a small town in Washington had gone on to become one of the 20th century's most significant industrial inventors. Of the products he would create, two would change the world dramatically. From raincoats to computers, Dr. Semon's ideas are at work in products used by a public too busy to notice. He doesn't care. He's too busy himself.

Now in his 90s, Waldo Semon continues to search for solutions to various problems. His insatiable appetite for learning has also not abated. Despite diminished eyesight, he continues to stay informed about leading-edge technologies and current events by listening to audio-taped readings of articles from scientific magazines and industry trade journals.

LEFT TO RIGHT — *David Bonner, former Vice President of Research and Development, BFGoodrich; William F. Patient, President, Chairman and CEO Geon; Donald P. Knechtges, Vice President-Commercial, Geon; Dr. Waldo Semon; and John Lauer, President and CEO, BFGoodrich (1991)*

Patents, Inventions and Awards

Semon, W.L., and Sloan, A. W. (Patent) ***Rubber Lining Pipe,*** **United States Patent Office #1,721,838 (1929).**
An elastic lining of rubber or flexible plastic can be adhesively applied to the interior of a hollow or tubular structure of metal or other rigid hollow object by (1) forming the lining in the size and shape it will finally occupy (2) turning the lining inside out (3) applying adhesive to the interior of the object and the exterior of the turned lining (4) by air pressure and mechanical action forcing the lining through an opening into the object whereby the lining is turned to its original configuration, the two adhesive surfaces being rolled together and establishing a blister-free contact between the lining and the object. If desired the construction can now be vulcanized to set the bond. The procedure and equipment for rubber lining steel pipes is described in detail.

Semon, W. L. (Patent) ***Method of Cleaning Metals,*** **United States Patent Office #1,756,311 (1930).**
In the steel industry rust and scale are remove from sheet, wire and pipe by pickling in hot sulfuric of hydrochloric acid. Normally in this process considerable iron is dissolved along with the oxides. The addition of about 0.5% of anilinobenzothiazole to the acid causes the development of a thin molecular protective coating on the surface of the iron which prevents solution of the metal in the acid.

Semon, W. L. and Crawford, R. A. (Patent) ***Dispersing Rubber in Water,*** **United States Patent Office #1,797,243 (1931).**
The power requirements for dispersing crude rubber in water are excessive. On the other hand if a low viscosity rubber cement is dispersed in water, the amount of dispersant required is sufficient to harm the properties of a rubber film deposited from such a dispersion. If 10 to 100 parts of a good solvent such as benzene are allowed to solvate each 100 parts of rubber and increase its plasticity, the product can now be dispersed in water easily using minimum amounts of soap and protective colloids. Films deposited from such a dispersion show superior properties for adhesive applications.

Semon, W. L. (Patent) ***Heel Lifts,*** **United States Patent Office #1,802,985 (1931).**
Celluloid or other polar plastic can be rigidly bonded to rubber, ebonite, metal or wood by adhering it to a fabric or fibrous interply using a proper polar adhesive and then bonding this plied up structure to the rubber, ebonite, metal or wood using an adhesive such as cyclo-rubber specifically suited for bonding fabric to these latter materials. This patent was used in the manufacture of heel lifts.

Semon, W. L. (Patent) ***Halogen Substituted Diarylamines as Anti-oxidants,*** **United States Patent Office #1,808,576 (1931).**
The deterioration of natural or synthetic rubber due to oxidation or cross-linking can be inhibited by the incorporation of 0.2 to 5% on the rubber of an antioxidant comprising a halogen substituted diarylamine. Para substitution shows a favorable activating effect, p-chlorophenyl-beta-naphthylamine is especially useful for reducing the deterioration of articles made from neoprene.

Semon, W. L., and Zimmerli, W. F. (Patent) ***Chewing Gum,*** **United States Patent Office #1,829,029 (1931).**
A Chewing gum base having properties similar to chicle can be made from a mixture, for example of: pale crepe natural rubber 20, white mineral oil 100, light magnesia 50, finely divided whiting 50 and water insoluble magnesium oleate 5 to 10 parts added to prevent the pigment from chewing out of the mixture. Sugar, flavoring and proprietary modifiers can be added to make a satisfactory commercial product. This is the basis for a "bubble gum."

Semon, W. L. (Patent) ***Method of Cleaning and Pickling Metals,*** **United States Patent Office #1,830,566 (1931).**
In the pickling of iron and steel, the rate of solution of the metal in the hot sulfuric or hydrochloric acid can be reduce by 95% by the addition of as little as 0.03% of an alkyl substituted pseudothiourea. 2-Phenylimino-3-phenyltetrahydro-thiazole prepared by reacting 1,2-dichloroethane with s-diphenylthi-ourea is especially active and has been used extensively as a pickling inhibitor and corrosion inhibitor. Because of its relative stability it can also be used with phosphoric, hydroflouric or even mixtures containing nitric acid.

Semon, W.L., and Zimmerli, W. F. (Patent) ***Latex Tubes,*** **United States Patent Office #1,841,076 (1932).**
Rubber articles can be manufactured from compounded rubber latex or rubber dispersions by spraying simultaneously the dispersed rubber compound and coagulant upon the surface of the desired form. Inner tubes, doll bodies, rubber gloves, gas masks, rubber shoes, etc. can be manufactured by this process.

Semon, W. L. (Patent) ***Method of Cleaning and Pickling Metals,*** **United States Patent Office #1,852,194 (1932).**
Heterocyclic compounds containing at least three different kinds of atoms in the ring are especially efficient in reducing the rate of solution of iron and steel in pickling acid. p-Hydroxy-N-phenyl morpholine rhodanic acid, thialdine, xanthane hydride and N-phenyl morpholine are cited as suitable example. This is a broad dominating patent in the field of pickling inhibitors.

Semon, W. L., (Patent) ***Binding Books,*** **United States Patent Office #1,856,685 (1932).**
An assembly of sheets of paper can be bound permanently into book form such that the leaves cannot be removed without tearing the paper by cutting a groove perhaps 1/16 in. deep every 1/8 to 1/2 in. along their back of the book, bending the cut sections of the leaves forward in the first section, backward in the second, forward in the third, etc, applying adhesive such as glue-glycerin compounded latex, or thermoplastic adhesive in such a manner that alternate sides of the cut and bent leaves are coated. A backing strip of paper or fabric may be adhesively applied to hold the cover in place.

Semon, W. L. (Patent) ***Resinous Antioxidants from Diarylamines Plus Formaldehyde,*** **United States Patent Office #1,860,434 (1932).**
It has been known the crystalline diarylamines are good anti-oxidants for use in rubber compounds. However, these materials have limited solubility and crystallize from the vulcanized rubber products. This invention consists in reacting such diarylamines with aldehydes to give high molecular weight resins of excellent antioxidant activity and high miscibility with rubber shown by freedom from crystallizing or blooming from the rubber stock. Examples include the reaction product or formaldehyde with phenylbeta-naphthylamine or diphenyl-p-phenylene diamine, or of aldol with p-amino diphenylamine.

Semon, W. L. (Patent) ***Diarylamines from p-Aminophenol as Antioxidants,*** **United States Patent Office #1,884,889 (1932).**
The crude reaction products formed by reacting an aminophenol with a primary aromatic amine are excellent antioxidants. Thus, when p-aminophenol is reacted with aniline, there is produced a mixture containing diphenylamine, p-hydroxydiphenylamine, p,p'-dihydroxydiphenylamine, N,N'-diphenyl-p-phenylenediamine, p,p'-dianilinodiphenylamine and higher condensation products. This crude tarry product is an outstanding anti-oxidant for use in tire treads. Production and use of this mixture has run into the tens of millions of pounds.

Semon, W. L. (Patent) ***Arylamides of Fatty Acids of Antioxidants,*** **United States Patent Office #1,886,310 (1932).**
The alylamides of fatty acids have the property of aiding the dispersion of pigments in rubber and at the same time imparting antioxidant activity. Oleanilide and stearanilide both exhibit these properties; however, even more active materials are obtained by forming amides from fatty acids and other aromatic amines such as naphthylamine, p-aminophenol, p-aminodiphenylamine.

Semon, W. L. (Patent) ***Reaction Products of Formaldehyde Plus Diarylamines as Antioxidants,*** **United States Patent Office #1,890,916 (1932).**
When diarylamines are reacted with formaldehyde there may be formed tetraphenyl methylenediamine, p,p'-dianilinodiphenylmethane, cyclic diarylamines or homologues depending upon the reactants. The individual compounds or crude products containing mixtures of the above are all excellent antioxidants of low volatility and small tendency to crystallize from the rubber.

Semon, W. L. (Patent) ***Reaction Products of Diarylamines with Aldehydes as Antioxidants,*** **United States Patent Office #1,890,917 (1932).**
When diarylamines are reacted with saturated or unsaturated aliphatic aldehydes containing more than two carbon atoms, there are produced crude

mixtures of excellent antioxidant properties for use in rubber. Twenty typical diarylamines are listed and their reaction products with fifteen typical aliphatic aldehydes. Excellent materials were formed by reacting diphenylamine with butyraldehyde, or di-phenylamine with alpha-etyl-beta-propylacrolein.

Semon, W. L. (Patent) *Plasticon Patent,* United States Patent Office #1,892,167 (1932).
When ground inner tube scrap or inner tube reclaim is fluxed at 350°F with a resin such as rosin or ester gum there is produced a permanently plastic adhesive. This may be thinned to a spreading consistency with a mixture of gasoline 2 parts and acetone 1 part.
Based upon this patent there was produce "Plasticon" adhesive which was sold in hundreds of thousands of gallons and used by the automotive and linoleum industries.

Semon, W. L. and Sloan, A. W. (Patent) *Method of Making Aldehyde Amines,* United States Patent Office #1,895,945 (1933).
The reaction product of aldol and alpha-naphthylamine sometimes referred to as crotonylidene alpha-naphthylamine is manufactured and sold as Age-Rite Resin. This patent describes a method for manufacturing this material and other similar aldehyde amines by metering the reactants to a heated continuous reactor and withdrawing the reacted product directly to shipping containers.

Semon, W. L. (Patent) *Rubber-set Brushes,* United States Patent Office #1,906,426 (1933).
This patent describes the method for manufacturing "rubber-set" brushes in which a bundle of bristles are placed in a ferrule. The rubber particles and sulfur penetrate between the bristles. Water is evaporated and the construction heated to permit the rubber and sulfur to react to form ebonite. The result is a brush in which the bristles are bonded and embedded in a matrix of solvent resistant hard rubber.

Semon, W. L. (Patent) *Antioxidants Containing Both Phenolic and Secondary Arylamino Groups,* United States Patent Office #1,919,452 (1933).
Both aromatic hydroxy compounds and secondary aromatic amines have been shown to have antioxidant activity in rubber. In this patent the two functions are combined in a single molecule leading to an accentuated effect. Some of the most effective mixed compounds are claimed in this patent, namely p-hydroxyphenyl-beta-naphthylamine, p-hydroxy-phenyl-alpha-naphthylamine and homologues.

Semon, W. L. (Patent) *Molecular Compounds of Phenols and Arylamines as Antioxidants,* United States Patent Office #1,921,007 (1933).
Phenols and amines upon admixture form loose molecular compounds having antioxidant activity in rubber exceeding that which could be obtained from either of the components separately. Those amines having a diarylamine structure and polyhydro-xyphenols are specified as components of the antioxidant complex. Phenyl-beta-naphthylamine + pyrogallol; N,N' diphenylethylene + hydroquinone and butylidene-alpha-naphthylamine + hydroquinone are cited among specific examples.

Semon, W. L., and Jones, P. C. (Patent) *Method for the Manufacture of Secondary Aromatic Amines,* United States Patent Office #1,921,587 (1933).
Small amounts of strong acid catalyze the reaction between primary aromatic amines and reactive phenols. Perhaps a dozen phenols and two dozen aromatic amines are cited to show how general the reaction is. Hydrochloric, sulfuric or sulfanilic acid are cited as typical acids. The reaction between beta-naphthol and aniline using sulfuric acid catalyst is described as a method for manufacturing phyl-beta-naphthylamine. Over 400 million pounds of phenyl-beta-naphthylamine have been manufactured by this process and sold as Age Rite Powder.

Semon, W. L. (Patent) *The Koroseal Patent — Plasticizer Polyvinyl Chloride,* United States Patent Office #1,929,453 (1933).
The Process of solvating a high molecular weight polymer of vinyl chloride with a relatively non-volatile polar solvent at a high temperature and cooling to form a flexible resilient gel.
This is the original plasticized polyvinyl chloride patent, use of which has led to the production, sale and consumption of over 2 billion pounds of polyvinyl chloride per year.

Semon, W. L. (Patent) *Diaryl-Phenylenediamines as Antioxidants,* United States Patent Office #1,940,815 (1933).
N,N-Diaryl-p-phenylenediamines are of outstanding activity as antioxidants for use in rubber. N,N'-Diphenyl-p-phenylenediamine has nearly the highest activity known as an antioxidant for use in rubber. N,N'-Di-beta-naphthyl-p-phenylenediamine has high activity and low staining properties when the rubber is exposed to light. Both of these have been manufactured, sold and used in large tonnages under the Age-Rite trademark. The beta-naphthyl derivative is used extensively as Age Rite White.

Semon, W. L. (Patent) *Thiodiarylamines as Antioxidants,* United States Patent Office #1,940,816 (1933).
When diarylamines are reacted with a sulfur there are formed thiazines. These are excellent antioxidants for use in rubber. Phenothiazine has been used especially in some of the synthetic rubbers and plastics. The bridging of two aryl rings with S ortho to the N.H.
Various groups or substituents may be attached to the two rings.

Semon, W. L. (Patent) *Salts of Complex Phenols with Amines as Antioxidants,* United States Patent Office #1,940,817 (1933).
Active antioxidants for use in rubber are obtained when phenols containing at least two aromatic nuclei are reacted with primary or secondary aliphatic or aromatic amines to form salts or loose molecular compounds. As examples may be cited o-phenylphenol plus dibutylamine; beta-naphthol plus diethanolamine; alpha-naphthol plus phenyl tolyamine beta-naphthol plus piperazine; p-phenylphenol plus p,p'-diamino diphenylmethane.

Semon, W. L. (Patent) *Diaryalmines Containing a Biphenyl Group as Antioxidants,* United States Patent Office #1,940,818 (1933).
Secondary aromatic amines containing a biphenyl groups are exceptionally good antioxidants for use in rubber. Typical examples are: diphenyl benzidine, di-beta-naphthyl benzidine; N-phenyl biphenylamine; di-p-biphenyl-p-phenylenediamine; tolyl-amino bitolyl; N,N'-2,5-diaminobiphenyl.

Semon, W. L. (Patent) *Secondary Amino Biphenyl Compounds as Antioxidants,* United States Patent Office #1,940,819 (1933).
This is a broad dominating patent covering in general "The method of preserving rubber which comprises treating rubber with a secondary amino biphenyl compound." 55 specific claims allowed.

Semon, W. L. (Patent) *Method of Recovering Amines and Phenols from Their Aqueous Solutions,* United States Patent Office #1,942,838 (1934).
Phenols and aromatic amines are often obtained in aqueous solution in the course of their manufacture. By forming suitable phenol-amine salts these materials may be precipitated from their aqueous solutions. Thus, by adding beta-naphthol to an aqueous solution p-phenylenediamine there is precipitated a salt which upon heating can be converted to di-beta-naphthyl-p-phenylenediamine. Conversely, if aniline is added to an aqueous solution of hydroquinone, a salt is precipitated which upon heating can be converted to N,N'-diphenyl-p-phenylenediamine. The process is of general value. Examples are given where it can be applied to 12 amines and 12 phenols.

Semon, W. L. and Zimmerli, W. F. (Patent) *The Oil-extended Rubber Patent,* United States Patent Office #1,942,853 (1934).
Compounding oils can be added to rubber without breaking down the molecular structure if the oil is applied to the surface of a thin sheet of crude unmasticated rubber and then time permitted for the oil to diffuse in the the rubber structure. Thus, comparatively non-tacky master batches which can be shipped and handled like ordinary crude rubber can be obtained with oil contents from 30 to 75%. Such master batches can be used to prepare high quality rubber products containing large proportions of oil since the rubber structure has not been mechanically degraded during the addition of the oil.

Semon, W. L. (Patent) *Alkoxydiarylamines as Antioxidants,* United States Patent Office #1,965,948 (1934).
Diarylamines containing alkoxy groups para to the nitrogen are not only excellent antioxidants for rubber but also increase the flexing life of the rubber article by a factor or from 8 to 10. Three or more carbon atoms in the alkoxy group are re-

quired in order to attain the highest activity. Thus both p-n-propoxy- and p-n-isoproxydiphenylamine are outstanding flexresister. p-Isobutoxydiphenylamine is comparable in activity. Thousands of tons of the p-isopropoxy derivative have been manufactured and sold under the Age Rite trademark.

Semon, W. L. (Patent) *Method of Removing Primary Aromatic Amines from Aqueous Solution,* United States Patent Office #1,968,913 (1934).
This patent is similar to U.S. Patent 1,942,939 but applies only to removing primary aromatic amines such as aniline from solution.

Semon, W. L. (Patent) *Antioxidants,* United States Patent Office #1,968,914 (1934).
This is similar to U.S. Patent 1,940,817 except that the field is expanded to claim a wider range of compounds such as; p,p'-dihydroxy diphenyldimethylmethane plus phenylnaphthylamine.

Semon, W. L. (Patent) *Latex Tubes,* United States Patent Office #1,969,101 (1934).
This describes a method for manufacturing shaped rubber articles in a continuous succession by spraying compounded latex upon the mold, partially drying and continuing the addition of sprayed coats until the desired thickness is built up. The articles are then dried on the same conveyor. This machine was used for making inner tubes, gloves and other articles suitable for such a process.

Semon, W. L. (Patent) *Mixtures of Diarylamines as Antioxidants,* United States Patent Office #1,975,734 (1934).
Antioxidants composed of mixtures of N,N'-diphenyl-p-phenylenediamine and diarylamine are especially active in retarding the deterioration of rubber. The following mixtures showed special value:

Diphenylamine	75%
N,N'-Diphenyl-p-phenylene diamine	25%
Phenyl-beta-naphthylamine	Major
N,N'-Diphenyl-p-phenylene diamine	Minor

The method for preparing the first mixture by a single chemical reaction is described. The latter mixture was sold in large tonnages under the name of Age Rite HP (High Powered).

Semon, W. L. (Patent) *Method of Manufacturing Secondary Aromatic Amines,* United States Patent Office #1,980,102 (1934).
Upon heating together for 2 to 10 hours at 250°C mixtures of aniline hydrochloride and p-aminophenol hydrochloride, pouring into water and neutralizing, there is obtained mixtures containing diphenylamine, p-hydroxydiphenylamine, p,p-dihydroxydiphenylamine, p-hydroxydiphenyl-p-phenylenediamine, N,N'-diphenyl-p-phenylenediamine and more complex molecular species. The proportion of the final products can be varied by varying the conditions of the reaction, hence this process can be used for preparing any of the above compounds desired.

Semon, W. L. (Patent) *Method of Polymerizing Vinyl Chloride,* United States Patent Office #1,983,949 (1934).
The polymerization of vinyl chloride using a peroxide catalyst can be greatly accelerated in the presence of solvents such as 1,1-dichloroethylene, 1,1,2-trichloroethane, acrolein or formaldehyde. (At the time it was thought that the added compounds merely activated the polymerization. Now it is known that actual copolymerization occurred.)

Semon, W. L. (Patent) *Ketone Primary Aromatic Amine Reaction Products as Antioxidants,* United States Patent Office #2,000,039 (1935).
Condensation products of ketones with primary aromatic amines are excellent antioxidants for use in rubber. Examples specifically mentioned are:

Cyclohexanone + alpha-napthylamine
Mesityl oxide + alpha-naphthylamine
Diacetone alcohol + aniline

A broad patent for which 58 claims were allowed.

Semon, W. L. and Sloan, A. W. (Patent) *Antioxidants,* United States Patent Office #2,000,040 (1935).
This is an extension of U.S. Patent 2,000,039 to include primary aromatic amines having alkyl or alkoxy substituents and specifically the reaction product of acetone with aniline.

Semon, W. L. (Patent) *Antioxidants,* United States Patent Office #2,000,041 (1935).
This is another extension of U.S. Patent 2,000,039 to include reaction products of ketones with amino-diarylamines. Specifically

acetone + aminodiphenylamine
acetone + diaminodiphenylamine

Semon, W. L., and Ford, T. F. (Patent) *Manufacture of Mercapto Aryl Thiazoles,* United States Patent Office #2,001,587 (1935).
When aniline is reacted with carbon disulfide and sulfur under pressure in order to form mercaptobenzothiazole there is a tremendous evolution of hydrogen sulfide. If in place of using sulfur as the oxidant, nitrobenzene is used, the reaction occurs at a lower temperature and no hydrogen sulfide is evolved. Thus, aniline 5 mols. nitrobenzene 2 mols. and carbon disulfide 6 mols. when heated for six hours at 220°C give an excellent yield of mercaptobenzothiazole.

Semon, W. L. (Patent) *Antioxidant,* United States Patent Office #2,009,526 (1935).
N-N'-Diphenyl-1, 4-naphthalenediamine is particularly effective as an antioxidant for retarding the deterioration of rubber. Homologues are also claimed.

Semon, W. L. (Patent) *The Age Rite Gel Patent,* United States Patent Office #2,013,319 (1935).
Microcrystalline petroleum wax having a melting point of 68°C has only a limited solubility in rubber at room temperature hence tends to bloom from cured rubber and yield a thin continuous film of wax. This film protects rubber from deterioration initiated by light. A combination of wax with diarylamine affords extra protection since the wax moving to the surface brings antioxidant along with it. Combinations of wax with N,N'-diphenyl-p-phenylene or ditolylamine are outstanding. A combination of microcrystalline wax (MP 68°) 20% with liquid mixed ditolylamines 80% is a gel which is easy to handle and in addition to being a double acting preservative also contributes a pleasing finish to the molded rubber article. This mixture was manufactured and sold in large volume as Age Rite Gel.

Semon, W. L. (Patent) *Method for Preparing Antioxidants,* United States Patent Office #2,015,696

This is a basic patent describing the chemistry of the formation of a new class of antioxidants by the reaction of a ketone with a primary of secondary aromatic amine in tw stages. The chemistry is described first for acetone + aniline, then acetone + diphenylamine and then extended to homologues. Essential intermediates are p'p-diaminodiphenyl-dimethylmethane and p,p'dianilinodiphenyl-dimethylmethane.

Semon, W. L. (Patent) *Tetraarylthiuram Sulfides,* United States Patent Office #2,026,256 (1935).
This patent describes a new reaction leading to a new class of organic compounds which have value as accelerators for the vulcanization of rubber. Diarylamines react with sodium metal to give compounds such as R_2N-Na. This in turn reacts with CS_2 to give R_2-N-CS-S-Na. By known methods the diaryldithiocarbamates can be converted into thuiram sulfides or polysulfides.

Semon, W. L. (Patent) *Method of Making Secondary Aromatic Amines,* United States Patent Office #2,029,642 (1936).
This is a continuation of U.S. Patent 1,942,838 in which the amine salt is heated to convert it by dehydration into a diarylamine.

Semon, W. L. (Patent) *Antioxidants,* United States Patent Office #2,035,620 (1936).
This is a division of U.S. Patent 1,940,816 in which diarylamines are reacted with sulfur or sulfur chlorides to dithio derivatives of value as antioxidants for rubber.

Semon, W. L. (Patent) *Ortho Bridged as Antioxidants,* United States Patent Office #2,037,932 (1936).
Diarylamines having a carbon bridge ortho to the NH group are outstanding antioxidants for use in rubber. Even when the aromaticity is reduced by hydrogenation, the activity persists. Such compounds include acridanes and hydroacridanes.

Semon, W. L. (Patent) *Preparation of Secondary Amines,* United States Patent Office #2,041,782 (1936).
Excellent antioxidants for rubber or secondary aromatic amines for other purposes may be prepared by the following reactions:

Aromatic amine –> diazotize –> couple with a phenol –> p-hydroxyazobenzene. Reduce –> original aromatic amine + a p-aminophenol HCl/heat –> mixture of a p-hydroxydiphenylamine and a diaryl-p-phenylene-diamine. Aromatic amine –> drazotize –> couple with an aromatic amine –> a diazamino-benzene HCl/rearrange –> a p-aminoazobenzene. Reduce –> original aromatic amine + a p-phenyl-enediamine HCl/heat – > a p-aminodiphenylamine and a diaryl-p-phenylenediamine.

Semon, W. L. (Patent) *Preparation of Aromatic Dithiocarbamates,* United States Patent Office #2,046,884 (1936).
The method of forming an aryl dithiocarbamate which consists in reacting a diarylamine with sodium, then reacting with carbon disulfide, extracting a crystallizing the sodium salt from water. A description is given of the large scale preparation of sodium diphenyldithiocar-bamate.

Semon, W. L. (Patent) *Antioxidant,* United States Patent Office #2,048,822 (1936).
Further examples to supplement U.S. Patent 2,015,696.

Semon, W. L. (Patent) *Antioxidant,* United States Patent Office #2,048,823 (1936).
This is a continuation of U.S. Patent 1,940,815 in which the phenylene ring of a diaryl-p-phenylenediamine contains a hydrocarbon subsistent. Antioxidants of this type are of extremely high activity and have a reduced tendency to bloom from the cured rubber article.

2, 5-Dianilinobiphenyl
2, 5-Dianilinocyclohexylbenzene
2, 5-Dianilinotoluene

Semon, W. L. (Patent) *Antioxidants,* United States Patent Office #2,053,785 (1936).
This is a continuation of U.S. Patent 1,940,815. Ditolyl-p-phenylenediamine.
This material is still being manufactured and used in large tonnage because it has low blooming characteristics and protects rubber from ozone.

Semon, W. L. (Patent) *Complex Diarylamines as Antioxidants,* United States Patent Office #2,061,779 (1936).
Antioxidants of unknown structure but of high activity in rubber are obtained by heating p,p'-dihydroxy-diphenyldimethylmethane with a primary aromatic amine using an acid catalyst. Pheno and ammonia re evolved, leaving a mixture of complex diarylamines. The phenol is reacted with acetone and recycled.

Semon, W. L. (Patent) *The Dialkyl-p-phenylenediamine Antiozonant Patent,* United States Patent Office #2,067,686 (1937).
The N,N' dialkyl p-phenylendiamines are excellent antioxidants for rubber, (They also show a pronounced antiozonant effect.)
The entire range of compounds from methyl to heptyl derivatives is disclosed as active. The N,N'-dibenzyl-p-phenylenediamine is claimed specifically. This is the "Antiozonant Patent". The dihexyl and the di-2-octyl derivatives have found large tonnage use especially in SBR tires.

Semon, W. L., and Yohe, R. V. (Patent) *Method for Preparing Aliphatic Aromatic Ethers,* United States Patent Office #2,070,848 (1937).
This describes a method whereby 90% of theoretical yields can be obtained by heating the sodium salt of a phenol in aqueous solution with an alkyl chloride. Thus, p-isopropoxydiphenylamine can be prepared from p-hydroxydiphenylamine and isopropyl chloride. This process has been extensively used on a tonnage manufacturing scale.

Semon, W. L. (Patent) *Diarylamines with Olefinic Substituents as Antioxidants,* United States Patent Office #2,075,549 (1937).
Diarylamines having an unsaturated aliphatic side chain are especially good antioxidants for rubber and other oxidizable organic material. From the many possible compounds listed p-isopropenyl-diphenylamine is selected for a specific claim.

Semon, W. L. (Patent) *Quinone-Amine Reaction Products as Antioxidants,* United States Patent Office #2,089,302 (1937).
The complex mixture obtained by reacting quinones with primary aromatic amines with elimination of water are good antioxidants for rubber. Specific products are:

quinone + aniline
aurine + aniline

Semon, W. L. (Patent) *Antioxidants,* United States Patent Office #2,097,473 (1937).
Ether or thioether substituted diarylamines are excellent antioxidants. Specifically listed are:

p-Phenylaminodiphenylether
pcp'-Di (phenylamino) diphenylether
Di (phenylamino) diphenylsulfide
Di (naphthylamion) diphenylsulfide

Semon, W. L. (Patent) *Antioxidants,* United States Patent Office #2,097,474 (1937).
Alkyloxydiphenyl-p-phenylenediamines are excellent antioxidants for rubber. Specifically mentioned are:

N-Phenyl-N'-p-anisyl-p-phenylenediamine
N,N'-Di-p-anisyl-p-phenylenediamine

Semon, W. L., and Yohe, R. V. (Patent) *Antioxidants,* United States Patent Office #2,103,188 (1937).
Bis-arylamino-aryloxyalkanes are excellent low staining antioxidants. A good "non-staining" antioxidant.

Semon, W. L. (Patent) *Secondary-tertiary Amino Antioxidants,* United States Patent Office #2,115,473 (1938).
Antioxidants having a secondary and tertiary amino group attached to the same aromatic ring have unexpectedly high activity for retarding the deterioration of rubber. Specifically

Trimethyl-p-phenylenediamine
p-Dimethylaminodiphenylamine
p-Dimethylaminophenyl-beta-naphthylamine
p-Dicyclohexylaminodiphenylamine
p-Dibenzylaminodiphenylamine
p-Phenylaminotriphenylamine

Semon, W. L. (Patent) *Method of Making Quinone Di-imides,* United States Patent Office #2,118,826 (1938).
The method for preparing quinone di-imides by grinding together the corresponding diamine and alkali in the presence of air in a heated ball mill. Thus, N,N'-diphenyl-p-phenylenediamine gives diphenyl-p-benzoquinonediimide and N,N'-di-beta-naphthyl-p-phenylenediamine gives the brick red di-beta-naphthyl-p-benzoquinonediimide. MP 345°C.

Semon, W. L. (Patent) *Method of Making Quinone Di-imides,* United States Patent Office #2,118,827 (1938).
In the preparation of quinone di-imides if a catalytic metal oxide is included along with the alkali, the reaction runs more smoothly and rapidly. The preferred metal oxide is Pb0.

Semon, W. L. (Patent) *Complex Diarylamine Antioxidant,* United States Patent Office #2,166,223 (1939).
A product suitable for retarding the oxidation of organic substances can be prepared by heating together an aromatic amine, an alcohol and an oxidizing agent.
Diphenylamine, isopropanol, nitrobenzene and conc. HCl heated six hours at 259°C.
Aniline, ethylene glycol, nitrobenzene and conc. HCl heated four hours at 259°C.
Stearyl alcohol, aniline, azobenzene and zinc chloride.

Semon, W. L. (Patent) *Accelerator of Vulcanization,* United States Patent Office #2,170,037 (1939).
Excellent accelerators for the vulcanization of rubber are prepared by reacting the sodium derivative of meso-dimethylacridane with CS_2 then making the zinc salt of the dithiocarbamate, the dinitrophenylester or the disulfide.

Semon, W. L., (Patent) *Method of Stress-relieving Plastics,* United States Patent Office #2,176,153 (1939).
The oriented stresses built in to a film of plasticized polyvinyl chloride can be relieved by floating the film across the surface of a pool of mercury heated to 150°C.

Semon, W. L. (Patent) *The Platisol Patent,* United States Patent Office #2,188,396 (1940).
A paste or putty can be made from powdered polyvinyl chloride, polar plasticizer and pigment. After spreading or forming, the product can be set up to a resilient rubberlike product by heating until the polyvinyl chloride has just dissolved and then causing the composition to gel by cooling it.

Semon, W. L. (Patent) *Vulcanization Activators,* United States Patent Office #2,188,420 (1940).
A quaternary ammonium salt of a fatty acid is an excellent activator for a number of organic accelerators for the vulcanization of rubber. Tetramethylammonium oleate. Trimethylphenyl-ammonium oleate.

Semon, W. L. (Patent) *Double Compounds from Diarylamines and Acridines as Antioxidants,* United States Patent Office #2,193,650 (1940).
Acridines and diarylamines form definited mo-

lecular compounds which have very good antioxidant activity in rubber.
Acridine-diphenylamine MP 84-86°C; meso-Methyl acridine-diphenylamine Mp 98-100°C.

Semon, W. L. (Patent) *Accelerator of Vulcanization,* United States Patent Office #2,193,651 (1940).
The polynitrophenyl esters of diaryl dithiocarbamates are excellent delayed action accelerators. $(C_6H_5)_2$ N-CS-S-2,4-dinotrophenyl.

Semon, W. L. (Patent) *Esters of Diaryldithiocarbamates as Accelerators,* United States Patent Office #2,193,652 (1940).
The aldehyde condensation products of diaryldithiocarbamates are excellent accelerators for use in the vulcanization of rubber.
(C_6H_5)2 N-CS-S-CH_2-S-CS-N $(C_6H_5)_2$
Also similar products from phenyl-alpha-sponding beta derivative.

Semon, W. L. (Patent) *Accelerator of Vulcanization,* United States Patent Office #2,193,653 (1940).
Arylalkylidene bis esters of diaryl dithiocarbamic acid are of exceptional value as rubber accelerators because of their delayed action which permits mixing and handling of the rubber stock without scorching.
Three compounds are claimed specifically
Benzal-bis-diphenyldithiocarbamate
Benzal-bis-phenyl-alpha-naphthyldithiocarbamate
Benzal-bis-phenyl-beta-naphthyldithiocarbamate

Semon, W. L. (Patent) *Accelerator,* United States Patent Office #2,193,654 (1940).
The dialkyldithiocarbamic acids are extremely unstable, decomposing at room temperature. On the other hand the diaryl dithocarbamic acids are quite stable and can be used as vulcanization accelerator for rubber. Diphenyldithiocarbamic acid MP 140°C. Phenyl-beta-naphthyldithiocarbamic acid MP 143°C.

Semon, W. L. (Patent) *Accelerator of Vulcanization,* United States Patent Office #2,193,655 (1940).
This patent claims as delayed action accelerators for vulcanization the benzothiazyl esters of diaryldi-thiocarbamic acids. Specifically claimed are the 6-nitrobenzothiazyl esters of diphenyl-,phenylalphanaphthyl- and phenyl-beta-naphthyldithiocarbamic acid.

Semon, W. L. (Patent) *Accelerator,* United States Patent Office #2,193,656 (1940).
This patent claims the alkali metal salts of diaryldithiocarbamic acid as accelerators for the vulcanization of rubber. Specifically the sodium salts of diphenyl-, phenyl-alpha-naphthyl- or phenyl-beta-naphthyldithiocarbamic acid.

Semon, W. L. (Patent) *Continuous Reactor for Corrosive Pressure Reactions,* United States Patent Office #2,204,156 (1940).
This describes a vessel in which reaction in a highly corrosive medium can be carried out continuously at high pressure (600 to 1000 psi) and high temperature (250 to 350°C). In this reactor diphenylamine (or di-p-tolyamine) can be prepared continuously by the reaction in concentrated aqueous solution of aniline with aniline hydrochloride at 310°C., 700 psi with a yield of better than 96% of theory.
The reactor consists of an inner glass or ceramic tube vented thru a ceramic reducing valve made for instance from a spark plug. This floats in a steel pressure tube thru the walls of which the reactants are heated. The non-corrosive reactant is pumped in continuously between the steel shell and the ceramic tube. This material absorbs the heat from the exterior shell and protects it from corrosion as it flows around the interior ceramic tube and enters this tube at the end of the reactor opposite to the ceramic reducing valve. The corrosive readant is pumped in continuously thru a small ceramic probe which projects into the floating ceramic tube. Reaction occurs inside the floating ceramic tube without contact with the steel shell.

Semon, W. L. (Patent) *Dehydration Catalyst,* United States Patent Office #2,204,157 (1940).
The process for preparing an aluminum phosphate catalyst (with or without activator consisting of Zn, Fe, Mn, Cd, Cu, Mg, Ca, Ba, Sr, ions) and graphite or red phosphorus activator. This catalyst is especially suitable for dehydrating alcohols and in the case of 1,3-butanediol at 285°C gives a yield of over 75% of butadiene.

Semon, W. L. (Patent) *Aryl Decahydronaphthylamine Antioxidants,* United States Patent Office #2,206,433 (1940).
Cured rubber articles may be protected from the harmful effects of oxidation if a small amount of an aryl decahydronaphthylamine is incorporated.
Phenyl-beta-decahydronaphthylamine
Phenyl-alpha-decahydronaphthylamine
Beta-naphthyl-beta-decahydronaphthylamine

Semon, W. L, and Wellman, V. E. (Patent) *Hydrogenation Catalysts,* United States Patent Office #2,208,616 (1940).
In the process of hydrogenating aldo to 1,3-butanediol by passing a mixture of aldol and hydrogen gas over an active nickel catalyst, the catalyst slowly loses its activity. It can be reactivated by washing with water then anodically oxidizing in sodium hydroxide solution, washing with water and reducing with hydrogen. In this process adsorbed organic material is oxidized and completely separated from the nickel.

Semon, W. L. (Patent) *Hydrogenated Diarylamino Reaction Products as Antioxidants,* United States Patent Office #2,218,661 (1940).
When diarylamines are reacted with aldehydes or ketones at perhaps 250°C, there are obtained products of tarry character and bad odor. If these mixtures are partially reduced with hydrogen under pressure there are obtained products of more oily or crystalline character having a light straw color and a pleasing odor. These reduced products are superior antioxidants for use in rubber.

Semon, W. L. (Patent) *Cobalt for Adhering Rubber,* United States Patent Office #2,240,805 (1941).
Vulcanized rubber stocks can be bonded to metal by vulcanizing a rubber compound under pressure against a metal having a cobalt surface. Cobalt plating is a desirable method for developing the active cobalt surface which need be only 8 x 107 cm in thickness.
Details for the rubber stock, the adhesion cement and the method of plating are given.

Semon, W. L. (Patent) *Method of Activating Catalysts,* United States Patent Office #2,253,871 (1941).
The method of activating a massive nickel catalyst which consists in developing an active surface. This is done by electrolytic anodic oxidation of nickel shavings contained in a monel wire cage using a mixture of alkali hydroxide and carbonate at a pH of 11 to 13.5. Following the formation of the higher oxide film on the surface, the catalyst is washed in water and reduced with hydrogen to develop the maximum activity.

Semon, W. L., and Schoenfeld, F. (Patent) *Method for Continuous Polymerization,* United States Patent Office #2,259,180 (1941).
The method of polymerization vinyl chloride (butadiene or mixtures with suitable comonomers) which consists in emulsifying the monomers and initiator in aqueous vehicle under pressure. This emulsion is now pumped to the bottom of a very long vertical tube such that the hydraulic pressure of the liquid in the tube at all points exceed the vapor pressure of the unpolymerized monomers in the emulsion. Polymerization occurs progressively as any portion of the emulsion moves up the tube. Latex or disperison of the polymer flows continuously from the top of the tube. The hydraulic height of the tube may have to be 100 to 500 ft. hence the tube may be sunk in a well in the ground.

Semon, W. L. (Patent) *Mercaptoquinoline Derivatives as Accelerators,* United States Patent Office #2,279,875 (1942).
New and highly active accelerators for the vulcanization of rubber are base don 2-mercaptoquinoline.
This material, its oxidation product the disulfide, its zinc salt, its salt with diphenylquanidine are all excellent accelerators. Various homologues and substitution products also show this same high activity.

Semon, W. L. (Patent) *Emulsifiers for Polymerization,* United States Patent Office #2,315,664 (1943).
Soaps of fatty acids are often used as emulsifying agents in making synthetic rubbers. After the latex has been stabilized with antioxidant the

rubber and fatty acid are coagulated with dilute mineral acid. The fatty acid can be separated from the crub by extraction with dilute aqueous alkali. Fatty acid or soap recovered in this manner cannot be reused since it completely inhibits polymerization of fresh monomers. If the acid is converted to methyl esters using HCl catalyst, the ester separated from the aqueous phase and distilled in a vacuum, there is obtained methyl ester free from inhibiting substances. This ester can be saponified with NaOH and the aqueous soap solution reused for the manufacture of more synthetic rubber. This is especially important when an expensive fatty acid such as myristic acid is utilized in making superior grades of synthetic rubber.

Semon, W. L. (Patent) *Softener for Synthetic Rubber.* Borate Ester Softeners, United States Patent Office #2,325,985 (1943).
Synthetic rubbers made as copolymers of butadiene and a highly polar comonomer e.g. acrylonitrile require softeners having a high degree of polarity. Esters of boric acid with higher alcohols are especially good softeners Polymers.

Semon, W. L., (Patent) *Purification of Nitriles,* United States Patent Office #2,351,157 (1944).
Acrylonitrile as prepared from ethylenecyanohydrine, cyanethyl acetate or acetylene plus hydrogen cyanide is difficult to purify sufficiently so that it can be copolymerized with butadiene. If unsatisfactory acrylonitrite from these processes is agitated with sufficient aqueous cupric hydroxide so that a slight blue color persists, then steam distilled, the azeotrope is free from harmful inhibiting impurities and can be used directly in making copolymers with butadiene.

Semon, W. L. (Patent) *Purification of Mercaptans,* United States Patent Office #2,355,335 (1944).
In the manufacture of higher mercaptans for use as modifiers in the manufacture of synthetic rubber, the commercial products often contain varying amounts of the corresponding alcohols as impurities. If excess boric acid is added to such a mixture, the alcohol forms a relatively non-volatile borate ester. The residue containing the borate ester can be hydrolyzed with water and the oily alcohol separated for reprocessing. The boric acid can also be reused in the process.

Semon, W. L. (Patent) *Terpolymer Rubbers,* United States Patent Office #2,334,571 (1945).
Favorable combinations of properties can be obtained by copolymerizing butadiene with two or more comomers one of which is an acrylate. Examples:

Butadiene	Butadiene
Acrylonitrile	Acrylonitrile
Ethyl acrylate	Butyl acrylale

Semon, W. L., and Craig, D. (Patent) *Purification of Butadiene,* United States Patent Office #2,366,361 (1945).
This covers the batch method for the the purification of butadiene from the petroleum sources using extractive distillation. Solvents: Furfural and water, mesilyl oxide and water, etc. The batch process is much easier to control than the continuous process of U.S. Patent #2,366,360.

Semon, W. L., and Craig, D. (Patent) *Purification of Butadiene,* United States Patent Office #2,366,362 (1945).
The process for purification of butadiene from petroleum sources using extractive distillation with acetone. Other solvents; n-butyraldehyde, methyl ethyl ketone.

Semon, W. L. (Patent) *Purification of Butadiene,* United States Patent Office #2,366,369 (1945).
This patent covers the continuous method still used for purifying butadiene from hydrocarbon sources by extractive distillation. Solvents-Furfural and water, Nitrobenzene and acetone,2,2-Dichlorodiethylether and methanol, etc. This is the continuous process.

Semon, W. L. (Patent) *Method of Coagulating Dispersions. The Coagulation Patent,* United States Patent Office #2,366,460 (1945).
The method of coagulating synthetic rubber in the form of small crumbs by adding continuously synthetic rubber latex and coagulant to a highly turbulent coagulating region. This method is still used in the majority of synthetic rubber plants.

Semon, W. L., and Fryling, C. F. (Patent) *Stabilization of Butadiene-1,3 Hydrocarbons,* United States Patent Office #2,373,754 (1945).
The method for inhibiting the polymerization of butadiene during storage or shipment which consists in adding 0.001 to 0.1% of higher mercaptan to the butadiene. Butadiene so stabilized can be used without purification for the manufacture of butadiene polymers or copolymers in aqueous emulsion. Mercaptans with 6 to 10 carbons are preferred.

Semon, W. L., (Patent) *Copolymers of Acrylic Nitriles with Lesser Amounts of Conjugated Dienes,* United States Patent Office #2,374,841 (1945).
Highly oil-resistant, tough rubbery or leatherlike copolymers can be obtained by copolymerizing > 50 parts acrylonilele with< 50 parts of butadiene. More than 80 parts of acrylonitrile gives less valuable products. This copolymerization is performed in emulsion. In place of acrylonitrile, metha-crylonitrile can be used and isoprene or 2,3-dimethyl-butadiene in place of butadiene.

Semon, W. L., (Patent) *Stabilizing Synthetic Rubber Latex,* United States Patent Office #2,375,042 (1945).
Polymers and copolymers of butadiene have a tendency to toughen or cross-link upon storage. This tendency can be materially reduced by adding a small amount of ammonium dithiocarbamate and phenyl-beta-naphthylamine to the latex before the rubber is coagulated.

Semon, W. L. (Patent) *Emulsion Polymerization of Butadiene-1,3 Hydrocarbons, Alkyl Benzene Sulfonate Emulsifiers,* United States Patent Office #2,375,140 (1945).
In the process of making copolymers of butadiene with acrylonitrile or styrene the sodium salts of alkyl benzene sulfonic acids are superior emulsifying agents. The best products contain form 6 to 16 carbons in the side chain attached to the benzene.

Semon, W. L., and Fryling, C. F. (Patent) *Polymerization Initiators,* United States Patent Office #2,376,014 (1945).
The polymerization of butadiene along with acrylonitrile or styrene in aqueous emulsion can be initiated by the use of an aliphatic diazocompound. 0.5 to 1 part per hundred of polymer is required.

Potassium diazoacetate
Potassium diazomethane disulfonate

Semon, W. L., (Patent) *Polymerization Initiators,* United States Patent Office #2,376,015 (1945).
Triazenes are extremely efficient initiators for the polymerization and copolymerization of vinyl compounds in aqueous suspension. These are useful in making copolymers with butadiene.

$$R_1\,N = N - R_2\,R_3$$
$$1 \quad 2 \quad 3$$

Aliphatic triazines are especially good. 1-Phenyl-3,3-dimethyl triazene; 1,3 Diphenyl-3-methyl triazene are examples.

Semon, W. L. (Patent) *Polymerization of Butadiene-1,3, Modifiers,* United States Patent Office #2,376,390 (1945).
Copolymers of butadiene with acrylonitrile or with styrene when made in aqueous emulsion often tend to be crumbly and insoluble in organic solvents. The use of about 0.5% of a bis-thioxanthogen in the recipe gives rise to well modified polymers having good solubility and rubber properties

$$C_2H_5—S—CS—S—S—CS—S—C_2H_5$$

Isopropyl- and n-amyl-derivatives also claimed.

Semon, W. L. (Patent) *Modifiers,* United States Patent Office #2,376,391 (1945).
Copolymers of butadiene with acrylonitrile or with styrene when made in aqueous emulsion often tend to be insoluble and crumbly. The use of about 0.5% of a bis-anthogen disulfide in the recipe gives rise to modified polymers having good solubility and rubbery properties. Examples are:

Bis-ethylxanthogen
Bis-isopropylxanthogen
Bis-n-amylxanthogen
Bis-isobutylxanthogen

Semon, W. L., and Fryling, C.F., (Patent) *Removal of Fatty Acid from Synthetic Rubbers,* United States Patent Office #2,378,732 (1945).
A detailed discussion of the emulsion polymerization of butadiene with comonomers. A synthetic rubber free from fatty acid can be obtained by coagulating the synthetic rubber latex containing antioxidant in the form of fine crumbs and then extracting the fatty acid immediately with an aqueous solution of sodium hydroxide.

Semon, W. L. (Patent) ***Modifiers,*** **United States Patent Office #2,380,471 (1945).**
Superior butadiene copolymers can be prepared in aqueous emulsion if a modifier made by reacting an alkali metal xanthates with phosgene is used.

Semon, W. L. (Patent) ***Non-inhibiting Polymerization,*** **United States Patent Office #2,880,551 (1945).**
Polymerization of vinyl monomers or of butadiene with comonomers in aqueous emulsion has previously been carried out in glass coated vessels. If stainless alloys such as one from

Ni 80 to 70%
Cr 15 to 20%
Fe 5 to 10%

are used there is no inhibition of polymerization and negligible build up of polymer on the surface.

Semon, W. L., and Stewart, W. D. (Patent) ***Non-inhibiting Polymerization Vessels,*** **United States Patent Office #2,380,552 (1945).**
Iron surfaces often completely inhibit emulsion polymerization. If the ferrometallic vessel is treated so that a coating of insoluble iron phosphates is developed on the inner surface, then emulsion polymerizations may be carried out without inhibition and with minimum build up.

Semon, W. L. (Patent) ***Redox Activation of Polymerization,*** **United States Patent Office #2,380,614 (1945).**
Emulsion polymerization of butadiene with comonomers can be greatly accelerated by using a Redox catalyst. This catalyst however must be of high purity and complete reproducibility. A method is described for preparing potassium ferric oxalate in a high degree of purity. This dissolves in sodium pyrophosphate to give sodium ferric pyrophosphate of high activity in accelerating emulsion polymerizations.

Semon, W. L. (Patent) ***Polymerization Products,*** **United States Patent Office #2,384,568 (1945).**
A synthetic polymer obtained by copolymerizing butadiene with an ester having two unsaturated group.

Butadiene + allyl crotonate
Butadiene + diallyl phthalate
Butadiene + diallyl adipate

Semon, W. L. (Patent) ***Copolymers of Dienes and Olefinic Dicarboxylic Acid Esters,*** **United States Patent Office #2,384,569 (1945).**
A copolymer of butadiene with diethyl maleate.

Semon, W. L. (Patent) ***Polycomponent Copolymer Rubbers,*** **United States Patent Office #2,384,570 (1945).**
Favorable combinations of properties can be obtained by copolymerizing butadiene with two or more copolymers.
Examples:

Butadiene	Butadiene
Acrylonitrile	Acrylonitrile
Methacrylonitrile	Methyl methacrylate

Semon, W. L. (Patent) ***Copolymers of Butadiene-1,3 Hydrocarbons and Other Organic Compounds,*** **United States Patent Office #2,384,572 (1945).**
Copolymers of butadiene with diallylketone or allyl crotonate.

Semon, W. L. (Patent) ***Rubberlike Multipolymers,*** **United States Patent Office #2,395,017 (1945).**
A long descriptive patent giving 21 examples. Claimed specifically is the terpolymer from butadiene, acrylonitrile and an acrylic acid. Examples:

Butadiene	Butadiene
Acrylonitrile	Acrylonitrile
Ethatcrylic acid	Acrylic acid

Semon, W. L. (Patent) ***Copolymers of Butadiene-1,3 and N-Dialkyl Acrylamides,*** **United States Patent Office #2,401,885 (1946).**
Rubbery copolymers having interesting properties for certain specific uses can be made by copolymerizing butadiene with acrylamides. Specifically claimed is the copolymer made with butadiene and N-diethylacrylamide.

Semon, W. L. (Patent) ***Apparatus for Short Path Distillation,*** **United States Patent Office #2,460,602 (1949).**
A description is given of a rolling rod short path still in which fatty esters, rosin or "non-volatile" plasticizers may be distilled. Colored wood rosin can be distilled to give a water white rosin of high commercial value.

Semon, W. L. (Patent) ***Preparation of Alpha-Cyano Ester,*** **United States Patent Office #2,460,603 (1949).**
A new reaction has been discovered in which vinyl acetate reacts with acetone cyanhydrine in the presence of a trace of alkali catalyst to yield acetone and alpha-cyanoethyl acetate. This works also with homologues.

Semon, W. L. (Patent) ***Leaf or Vegetative Fertilizer. The Oxamide Patent,*** **United States Patent Office #2,663,629 (1953).**
Leaf feeding of certain amides from aqueous dispersion increases leaf growth on many plants, root growth on beets and yield of peas with pea vines.
Oxamide can be used as a lawn fertilizer. It has high nitrogen content which the plant can use as required. It is a completely non-burning fertilizer.

Semon, W. L. (Patent) ***The Cyclopolymerization Patent,*** **United States Patent Office #2,988,541 (1961).**
A wide variety of examples illustrating cyclopolymerization is given. By reacting an anhydrous acrylic acid with acetic anhydride under polymerizing conditions, there is produced a linear cyclo polymer. Many other methods are given.

$$
\left[-CH_2-\underset{\substack{| \\ O=C \\ O}}{CH}-CH_2-\underset{\substack{| \\ C=O}}{CH}- \right]_n
$$

and homologues.

AWARDS

Dr. Semon has received numerous awards during the course of his career, both in this country and throughout Europe. Among those he counts as most important to him:

1920 Graduates with honors, University of Washington.

1940 Modern Pioneer Award, National Association of Manufacturers.

1945 Charles Goodyear Medal (Rubber Science) American Chemical Society.

1946 Alumnus Summa Laude Dignatus University of Washington.

1960 Distinguished Member Award, Akron Science Society.

1964 3rd International Synthetic Rubber Gold Medal, London.

1964 Elliot Cresson Gold Medal, Franklin Institute.

1970 Thomas A. Midgley Award, American Chemical Society.

1982 Plastics Hall of Fame, Society of the Plastics Industry

1991 Material Manufacturer Industry Achievement Award, Plastics Hall of Fame, Society of the Plastics Industry